Workshop Materials

Workshop Materials
Alex Weiss

Special Interest Model Books

This book is dedicated to the memory of my good friend John Hearne, who first sparked my interest in model engineering

Special Interest Model Books Ltd.
P.O. Box 327
Poole
Dorset
BH15 2RG
England
www.specialinterestmodelbooks.co.uk

First published by Nexus Special Interest Ltd. 1999
This edition published by Special Interest Model Books Ltd. 2005
Reprinted 2009
© Special Interest Model Books Ltd. 2005

ISBN 978-1-85486-192-4

Printed and bound in Malta by Melita Press

Contents

Acknowledgements

It is not until you start writing a reference book that you come to realise how much you rely on other people for advice and help in gathering information. I am sincerely indebted to all of the following organisations. I hope I haven't forgotten to include anyone.

Columbia Metals for providing data on their range of specialist non-ferrous alloys.

CSM Abrasives who supplied me with two of the illustrations and a range of information used in Chapter 7.

Deluxe Materials (Models) UK for endless support in terms of illustrations and details about all of their adhesives.

Loctite UK for sending me a great deal of information about their engineering adhesives and their comprehensive range of lubricants and surface treatments.

Microflame Ltd for providing me with the photograph of their cutting discs.

Perma-grit for letting me use photographs of their tungsten carbide-coated tools.

ROCOL Ltd for providing me with data on their wide range of specialist lubricants.

I have also referred to a number of other volumes in the Workshop Practice Series as well as the late Tubal Cain's *Model Engineer's Handbook*, all of which proved to be useful sources of information.

Finally, I much appreciate my wife's acceptance of my obsessiveness in completing this volume.

Introduction

Materials used by model engineers

Model engineering is heavily reliant on the many and varied materials available today from a large number of different industries. These include the metal, wood, plastics, chemical and ceramics producers as well as those making adhesives, abrasives, fuels and lubricants to mention but a few.

This book describes the materials likely to be found in the average home workshop

Figure 1   Metal is the primary constructional material used by model engineers.

Name	Atomic no.	Symbol	Atomic wt.	Melt °C	Uses
Aluminium	13	Al	27	660	Alloy, raw material
Antimony	51	Sb	122	630	Hardening lead-based alloys
Argon	*18*	*A*	*40*	*- 189*	*TIG welding*
Arsenic	33	As	75	814	Hardening white bearings
Barium	56	Ba	137	704	Hardening lead bearings
Beryllium	4	Be	9	1280	Bronzes, electrical contacts
Bismuth	83	Bi	209	271	Small casting alloys
Boron	5	B	11	2300	Flux for silver soldering
Cadmium	48	Cd	112	321	Solder, copper alloys, plating
Calcium	20	Ca	40	850	Limestone and clays
Carbon	6	C	12	3700	Iron, steel, graphite, diamond
Chromium	24	Cr	52	1800	Plating, alloy steels
Cobalt	27	Co	59	1490	Cutting/tool steels, magnets
Copper	29	Cu	64	1083	Raw material, brass, bronze
Gallium	31	Ga	70	30	Solders, low-melt alloys
Gold	79	Au	197	1063	Plating, jewellery
Indium	49	In	115	156	Plating, specialist alloys
Iridium	77	Ir	193	2454	Delicate pivots, spark plugs
Iron	26	Fe	56	1535	Raw material, steels
Lead	82	Pb	207	327	Ballast, soft solders
Lithium	3	Li	7	186	Batteries, aluminium fluxes
Magnesium	12	Mg	24	650	Lightweight alloys
Manganese	25	Mn	55	1260	Steel alloys, bronzes
Mercury	80	Hg	200	-39	Thermometers, barometers
Molybdenum	42	Mo	96	2625	Alloy steels
Neodymium	60	Nd	144	840	Magnesium alloys, magnets
Nickel	28	Ni	59	1455	Alloy steels
Niobium	41	Cb	93	2000	Stainless/alloy steels, brass
Nitrogen	*7*	*N*	*14*	*- 210*	*Forming hard nitrides*
Oxygen	*8*	*O*	*16*	*-219*	*Welding*
Palladium	46	Pd	107	1554	Electrical contacts
Phosphorus	15	P	31	44	Phosphor bronze.
Platinum	78	Pt	195	1773	Coating delicate components
Rhenium	75	Re	186	3180	Tungsten alloys
Rhodium	45	Rh	103	1966	Thermocouples, furnace parts
Ruthenium	44	Ru	101	2450	Electronic wires, contacts
Samarium	62	Sm	105	1300	Magnets
Silicon	14	Si	28	1430	Abrasives, refractory material
Silver	47	Ag	108	961	Silver solder, silverware
Sodium	11	Na	23	98	Lamps, borax
Sulphur	16	S	32	119	Free-cutting steels
Tin	50	Sn	119	232	Bronzes, soft solder, tinplate
Titanium	22	Ti	48	1820	Alloy steels
Tungsten	74	W	184	3410	Alloy steels, tungsten carbide

Name	Atomic no.	Symbol	Atomic wt.	Melt °C	Uses
Vanadium	23	V	51	1735	**Alloy steels**
Yttrium	39	Y	89	1490	**Ceramic materials**
Zinc	30	Zn	65	420	**Galvanising, brasses**
Zirconium	40	Zr	91	1700	**Steels, sintered alloys**

Table 1 The elements which may be found in home workshops. Metals are in bold, non-metals in normal text and gases in italics. The atomic symbols are used as abbreviations in this book.

and indicates where they are normally used. The majority are metals which form the lifeblood of the hobby. It is beyond the scope of this volume to describe how to use the various materials. This is well covered by the many other volumes in the *Workshop Practice Series.*

All materials are made up of atoms, the basic building blocks of all matter. The majority are metals. These atoms, and there are 92 natural ones, are used either alone or in combination. The more common ones are listed in Table 1 together with their melting points and typical uses. They may be combined in mechanical mixtures or chemical compounds. These materials may exist at room temperature as solids, liquids or gases. Alloys are combinations, mixtures or solutions of elements and/or chemical compounds.

The key to the industrial revolution, and also to most model engineering tasks, was and is the availability of iron and steel. The latter in its various forms is the single most important metal available today. This does not mean that other

Figure 2 A splendid GWR locomotive boiler shows off its metallic finish prior to painting.

Figure 3 This traction engine features a copper boiler and steel gears.

materials like aluminium, brass, copper, even wood and plastics, do not have an important place in the hobby.

This book looks at the materials used, not only by the primary participants in the hobby of model engineering; locomotive, traction, boat and stationary steam engines, but also considers those worked by builders of internal combustion engines from oil, diesel, glow and petrol engines to gas turbines. It also considers clock makers, those who build workshop tools and minority interests like the construction of artillery pieces, farming appliances, carriages and other road vehicles. It also tries to cover the materials of interest to those whose hobby involves working with full-size machinery, such as vintage and veteran cars, motor cycles and their pedal-powered equivalents, full-size internal combustion engines, traction engines, railway locomotives and rolling stock.

Thus, solid materials come under one main category; metals, subdivided into three chapters covering iron and steel, aluminium and copper, and other non-ferrous metals; and two subsidiary ones: plastics and wood. There are also details of liquids like pickles and electroplating solutions and even gases like oxygen, acetylene and propane. In addition to the various materials used actually to make models, there is also a significant number of other substances which are found in many workshops. These include abrasives, adhesives, ceramics, composite materials, fuels and solders.

Definitions and standards

First, what is a metal and what is not? Table 1 shows which of the naturally occurring elements, commonly found in the home workshop, are metals. Although many metals are elements like copper or tin, many more are alloys such as steel and brass. Basic steel is an alloy of a metal, iron and a non-metal, carbon while brass is an alloy of two metals; copper and zinc. Many alloys contain a large number of different constituents. This still hasn't answered the basic question.

Metals are materials which shine when polished and are good conductors of heat and electricity. Most of them are strong and will withstand a degree of overload without catastrophic failure. They are more malleable and denser than non-metals and are crystalline substances.

Metals fall into two main grouping; ferrous metals and non-ferrous ones. The former include the various forms of iron and steel, and most of them are magnetic. The non-ferrous or non iron-containing metals comprise all the others. However, it is rare to find pure metals used either in everyday objects, or in the home workshop. Almost invariably, the metal will be in the form of an alloy, even though in the cases of aluminium, copper and iron, for example, the name of the pure metal is still used. However, for most people, the word alloy brings to mind a material like brass which is a mix of copper and zinc, or bronze, made from copper and tin.

An alloy is a combination of a metal, with one or more other metals or non-metals, to form a new metal. The result may be a compound, a mixture or a solid solution. Alloys are usually harder and stronger than their constituent metals and may also melt at lower temperatures.

In fact, their melting point is usually across a range of temperatures rather than at a single one. The characteristics of alloys are designed to provide the required combination of properties. As a result, there is continual development

Figure 4 A mixture of copper, brass and mahogany have been used in the construction of this boiler.

of new alloys with special attributes. This is particularly true of aluminium, copper and steel alloys.

Many metals are malleable and ductile because their structure allows individual particles within the material to slide over one another relatively easily. Metals are therefore easy to bend and form into new shapes. When working the metal, once a particle has moved into its neighbouring space it locks to adjacent particles and cannot continue to slide. As metal is cold worked, the particles take up their free movement and will eventually slip no further. The more a metal is worked, the harder it becomes; a phenomenon known as work-hardening. When running metals in close contact as, for example, in bearings or a piston/cylinder combination, it is accepted practice that dissimilar metals minimise wear when running.

One of the difficulties is that there are so many different grades of alloy and variants of each material. Take steel as an example. There is mild steel, carbon tool steel, high speed steel, silver steel and gauge plate. That might be sufficient choice for most model engineers, but perhaps not so for those building a model jet engine or aero engine when stainless and other alloy steels prove attractive.

For industrial purposes, there is a huge choice of materials in each category listed above. The choice will depend on the particular special mechanical and chemical properties needed to build the end product at the lowest possible cost. The average model engineer is unlikely to put excessive load on most materials used for building models and will not normally expose them to corrosive chemicals. The aim of this volume, therefore, is to offer a small selection of each type of material in the hope that this will satisfy 99.9% of needs, though a number of more specialised applications are also covered. The bibliography provides a source of further useful references.

Clearly the most popular metals in the home workshop are steel and iron, with copper, brass, bronze and aluminium following closely behind. In the first part of the book, each metal is examined in turn, giving a little background to the material followed by its main characteristics, useful parameters and available alloys. Chapter 4 then looks at selection and identification of materials.

Subsequent chapters look at two other raw materials; plastics and wood. Chapters 7 and 8 give detailed consideration of refractory materials, abrasives and joining materials including glues and solders. The next chapter is devoted to the liquids and their constituents used for cleaning, etching and plating processes. Finally, Chapter 10 deals with a range of other materials, mainly coatings, fuels, lubricants and gases.

The first two appendices examine some safety issues and provide a glossary of terms and abbreviations.

Metric units are used throughout this book as these units have inexorably taken over from imperial units in the production and processing of raw materials. For those who have yet to convert, or are building a model from old drawings, there are a number of conversion tables included in Appendix 3.

The last two appendices provide a list of useful addresses and relevant books, following which there is a comprehensive index.

CHAPTER 1

Iron and steel

Iron

The Iron Age, which followed the bronze age, began in the second millennium BC and lasted through until the end of the Middle Ages, though many people feel the iron age still continues. Even before the Industrial Revolution, some iron being made was in reality poor quality steel.

Iron is, without doubt, by far the most important metal produced and used by man. It is also the cheapest, accounting for as much as ninety percent of the world production of metal. It is one of the most abundant elements on earth and is found in nature in ores, such as hematite and magnetite. Pure iron is a relatively soft and ductile material, with a tensile strength of about $370N/mm^2$ and a density of around $7200kg/m^3$. It can be drawn into fine wires and rolled into thin sheets but has little practical use.

However, when iron is alloyed with carbon, a range of widely used and practical materials result, which have the widest applications in the home workshop. The percentage of carbon alloyed with the iron has an immense impact on the properties of the resulting metal.

It can be seen from Table 1.1 that the two commonly used forms of iron differ widely in terms of the amount of carbon they contain and also differ in that sense from steel.

The following terms are widely used to describe the alloys of iron. Ferrous alloys is the term used to describe all alloys of iron. Carbon steels are steel alloys which contain only iron and carbon, while the term alloy steel is used for those which include other elements as well.

Rust and damp protection

When iron and most forms of steel are left in a damp atmosphere, they will quickly form a surface layer of rust. This layer, reddish brown in colour, is the result of the formation of iron oxides.

Specially impregnated paper is available to help prevent the formation of rust. It may either be used to wrap the complete item, or a sheet placed in the container housing the iron or steel item.

Material	Carbon content
Wrought iron	0 – 0.05%
Steel	0.05 – 2%
Cast iron	2 – 4.3%

Table 1.1 The percentage of carbon alloyed with iron defines the final material.

1

Figure 1.1 Cast iron is a popular material for making cylinders and ports for steam engines.

Silica gel is a hard amorphous granular desiccant, usually contained in small linen bags. It is widely used as an absorbent to remove small quantities of water from the air in housings or other packaging where the contents will be affected by

Figure 1.2 The Stuart V10 steam engine comes as a set of castings. The main ones are of cast iron.

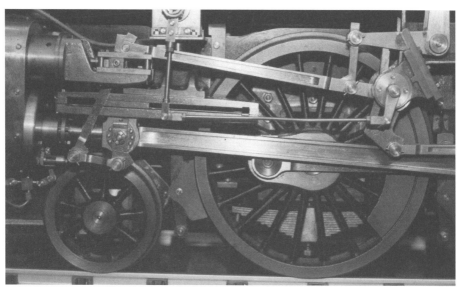

Figure 1.3 The classic mix of iron and steel shown in this locomotive's motion.

moisture. It can be regenerated by heating in an oven to drive off the water.

Pig iron

Iron is produced by heating iron ore with coke and limestone in a blast furnace to around 1800°C, then subjecting the hot mix to a blast of air to release the iron. The molten iron falls to the bottom of the furnace gathering impurities, mainly carbon, from the limestone and coke.

It then runs into open sand moulds, forming billets of pig iron, or the molten iron is taken to be made into steel. Pig iron solidifies at about 1130°C but is not a practical material, except as a basis for further refinement into grey or white cast iron.

Cast iron

With a carbon content of 2% or more, cast iron is available in two completely different grades:

Grey cast iron

Engineering cast iron normally contains 2% – 3.5% carbon. The cooling rate of the iron determines the form the carbon takes; graphite or iron carbide (cementite). Slow cooling preferentially produces graphite and a coarse-grained structure with a characteristic grey colour if the iron is fractured.

Grey iron containing graphite is more easily machined than the harder white form of cast iron. Grey cast iron is also softer, less brittle, cheap and melts at 1200°C. Use an HSS tool, with a cutting angle of around 10° to 12°, when working the material in a lathe and a cutting speed of 20m/min. Grey cast iron is not viscous when molten thus enabling complex shapes to be cast which are very strong in compression, less strong in tension and rather brittle. It cannot be bent or forged and is unsuitable for making cutting tools. It is good for machine

3

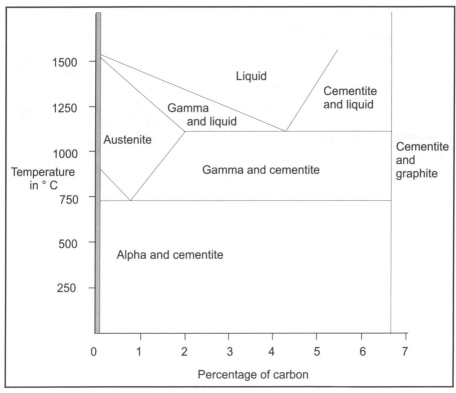

Figure 1.4 The relationship of the various forms of iron to temperature and carbon content.

frames, machine-tool beds and producing a range of castings for use in the home workshop. Typical tensile strength of grey cast iron is in the range 150–250N/mm².

White cast iron

If cooling is rapid, more carbon remains as carbide making the metal harder and whiter. White cast iron contains most of its carbon as cementite and has a whiter, closer-grained structure when fractured. White cast iron is hard, durable and very brittle with occasional hard spots where the metal has cooled too fast. It has little application in the home workshop.

Wrought iron

Virtually all the carbon in cast iron can be removed by reheating pig iron in a furnace and repeatedly mixing oxide with the molten metal. The carbon combines with the liberated oxygen and results in better than 99% pure iron, with small amounts of other elements. This is wrought iron.

It is a durable metal which bends quite easily when cold and resists damage from shock loads but is too soft to make cutting tools. It is a very popular material for ornamental work, although it needs a protective coating to avoid rusting.

4

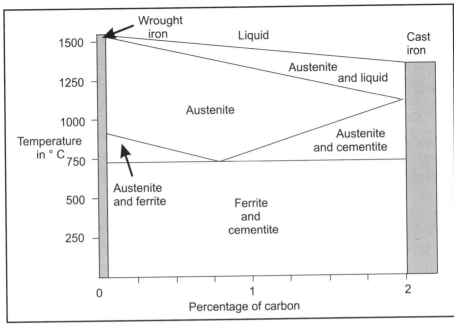

Figure 1.5 How the amount of carbon affects the resulting wrought iron, steel and cast iron.

Iron and steel constituents

Pure iron exists in three different forms, depending on the temperature. These are known as alpha, gamma and delta iron; the last existing only above 1403 °C.

Iron is invariably contaminated with a small amount of carbon, making it an alloy of iron and carbon. The amount of carbon and the method of production not only affects the properties of the resulting iron, but also defines whether it is a form of iron or a type of steel. Cast iron is very different both from mild steel and from wrought iron. About four fifths of iron production is in the form of plain carbon steel.

When iron is combined with a small amount of carbon the mechanical qualities of the resulting alloy will depend on how they are cooled. The main constituents are as follows:

Ferrite

This is a solution of carbon in alpha iron and contains from 0.008% carbon at 0°C to 0.8% at 723°C. It is a relatively soft and ductile material.

Austenite

This is a solid solution of carbon in gamma iron, varying from 0.8% at 723°C to 2.08% at 1148°C. It is a relatively soft material.

Cementite

This is iron carbide and contains 6.67% carbon. It is a hard but brittle compound.

Martensite

This is basically a super-saturated solid solution of carbon in ferrite. It has a low ductility and its hardness increases as the

5

carbon content rises. Rapidly quenched carbon steel, with up to 0.7% carbon, will convert it entirely into martensite. Above that percentage, the result will be a mixture of martensite and austenite.

Pearlite
This name has been given to a mixture of ferrite and cementite because, when examined under a microscope, the steel resembles mother of pearl. Pearlite is softer than martensite or bainite but harder and less ductile than ferrite.

Bainite
This is the name given to a mixture of ferrite plates and short cementite rods which occur when the cooling is too fast to produce pearlite.

Eutectoid point
Above the critical temperature of 723°C, cementite becomes unstable and, when slowly heated, is transformed into austenite and vice-versa. This temperature is called the eutectoid point and the structure of the material changes at this point.

Softening and hardening steel
Annealing involves heating a piece of steel to a high enough temperature to convert it entirely into austenite, and then slowly cooling it allowing the structure to convert to pearlite and ferrite. If the steel has more than one-third of a percent of carbon, rapid cooling by quenching results in a structural change and the formation of martensite, resulting in a much harder material. However, when cooling a bar of large cross-section, it is unlikely that the centre of the bar will cool sufficiently rapidly to allow the change to occur, so that the mechanical properties depend on the dimensions of the sample being heat treated.

Steel

Undoubtedly the key engineering material in the home workshop, steel is a low-cost yet extremely strong metal. It should be clear to anyone who has purchased cheap steel tools from the Far East, that there is 'steel' and 'steel'. The one has its constituent elements carefully controlled to provide the required properties, the other does not.

Before the mid 19th century, material with a carbon content halfway between wrought and cast iron was called steel and was made by the cementation process. Up to 15 tonnes of bars 75mm wide x 20mm thick were heated with charcoal for over a week at around 1000°C. The iron absorbed carbon right through the relatively thin bars. The carbon content was roughly controlled by the heating time but, unfortunately, varied between bars and within individual bars.

From the mid 18th century, following cementation the bars were remelted over a period of some five hours in special clay crucibles containing about 25kg of the material. The molten metal was then cast to form bars. Steel made by this process is called crucible or cast steel. By careful selection of the initial cemented bars, a far more uniform quality could be achieved than by previous methods. For very large items, the contents of several crucibles could be cast into a single sand mould. This steel could be hardened but was mostly used as a strong and tough raw material.

Most mild steel is still made in blast furnaces but high-carbon steel is usually made in an electric furnace. Here the carbon is added directly to the molten metal. Sophisticated methods of analysis are used to control quality.

Mild steel was originally considered to be a form of cast iron made by removing

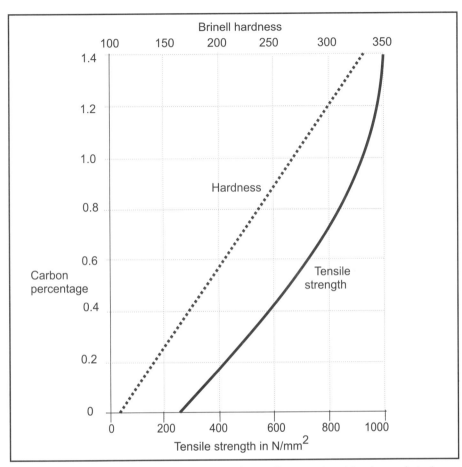

Figure 1.6 The effect of amount of carbon on the tensile strength and hardness of steel.

carbon: also avoiding slag inclusions. The Bessemer process blasts air through a container filled with molten iron to burn out the carbon. The later open hearth process, introduced about 1878, effected the conversion by reaction between the molten metal and the furnace lining.

Today, most mild or low carbon steel is made by blowing oxygen through a container holding some 300 tonnes of molten iron, brought directly from a blast furnace. Alloying elements including carbon are carefully added in the exact quantities needed.

It is interesting to look at some of the requirements of industry when selecting steel for drilling, milling or turning. The key factors are:

    1. Speed of metal removal.
    2. Length of tool life.

Carbon %	Typical uses
0	Nails, rivets, wire
0.2	Screws, tinplate
0.4	Con-rods, gears, shafts
0.6	Rails, screwdrivers
0.8	Cold chisels, shear blades
1.0	Drills, taps & dies
1.2	Broaches, files, reamers
1.4	Razor knife blades, saws

Table 1.2 The applications of carbon steel depend on the carbon content.

3. Power consumption.
4. Surface finish of component.
5. Chip form.
6. Ease of swarf removal.

Of these six factors, probably the one of greatest interest to the model engineer is surface finish, with most of the others some considerable way behind.

The application of steel to a particular task still depends crucially on the amount of carbon it contains and Table 1.2 lists typical uses.

The main additives making steel easier to cut are bismuth, calcium, lead, selenium, sulphur and tellurium. Sulphur is the cheapest and most widely used additive in making free-cutting steels. The inclusion of some manganese in these materials avoids cracking during hot working. Lead is the next most common additive but is now being replaced with bismuth due to health concerns associated with the use of lead. Similar problems with tellurium and its relative expense have reduced its popularity. Selenium is a common additive to stainless and alloy steels for improving machining characteristics, while calcium prevents the formation of hard alumina in steels containing aluminium.

Steel is a strong, magnetic material which enabled fast industrial progress during the second half of the nineteenth and the twentieth centuries. It is the primary material used by model engineers to make their models and is strong and relatively inexpensive. The only major problem with steel is its rapid rusting.

As stated, the contrast between steel and iron comes from the amount of carbon in each. Wrought iron is virtually carbon free.

Element	Improvement
Aluminium	Nitralloy suitable for nitriding.
Chromium	Corrosion resistance, ability to harden, abrasion/wear resistance, high temperature properties.
Cobalt	Strength at high temperature.
Copper	Corrosion resistance.
Lead	Free cutting.
Manganese	Ability to harden. With sulphur reduces brittleness.
Molybdenum	Ability to harden. Strength and toughness at room and high temperatures. Abrasion resistance.
Nickel	Strength and toughness.
Phosphorus	Free cutting.
Silicon	Strength of low alloy steels. Fluidity when casting.
Sulphur	Free cutting.
Titanium	Strong, tough chromium steels.
Tungsten	Strength and hardness at high temperatures. Abrasion-resistant tool steels.
Vanadium	Ability to harden at room and elevated temperatures.

Table 1.3 The impact of adding various elements to steel.

Material	Carbon content	Typical uses
Wrought iron	0 – 0.1%	Ornamental work
Mild steel	0.1 – 0.15%	Wire rod, thin sheets, solid drawn tubes
	0.15 – 0.25%	Boilers, general construction
Medium carbon	0.2 – 0.5%	Axles, high tensile tubes and wires
steel	0.5 – 0.7%	Springs, wire ropes, hammers
High carbon	0.7 – 0.9%	Springs, sheer blades, wood chisels
steel	0.9 – 1.1%	Cold chisels, taps and dies
	1.1 – 1.5%	Drills, metal cutting tools, files
Cast iron	2.5 – 4.5%	Casting, lathe beds

Table 1.4 The uses of iron alloy with different carbon contents.

Cast iron contains 2 – 5% carbon. Steel lies between these two extremes, normally containing 0.1 – 2% carbon.

Although steel often includes some other elements, carbon is by far the most important. Because of this, the classification of plain non-alloy steels depends on the carbon content. Mild steel normally contains 0.1% – 0.2% carbon; a medium carbon steel up to 0.7%. Both types can be toughened by heat treatment, though not sufficiently to make cutting tools.

High carbon steels contain 0.7% – 1.5% and are readily heat treated to provide excellent cutting tools. Above around 2.5% carbon, the resulting material is cast iron. Table 1.4 shows these materials in tabular form, together with typical uses.

Classification and types of steel

The old EN steel numbers started being used during World War II. As long ago as 1972, they were replaced by a new system of British Standard (BS) numbers that provide some useful information about the actual composition of the steel. However, materials specified to the old EN numbers are still to be found, particularly in model engineering circles.

BS 970 uses a six bit code, for example 070M20. The first three digits indicate several characteristics, shown in Table 1.5.

For example 190 is a plain carbon steel containing 0.9% manganese; 225 is free-cutting carbon steel with 0.25% sulphur. For stainless and alloy steels, the digits are unimportant for model engineers, though some correspond to the American AISI standards. The middle letter indicates the type of specification:

M – Particular mechanical properties.

A – Specific chemical analysis.

H – Particular ability to be hardened.

S – Stainless or heat resisting valve-steel.

It is not uncommon to find an identical material bearing a number in all of the first three categories.

The final two digits indicate the carbon content of all steels except stainless ones, where the numbers are arbitrary. For

BS code	Meaning
000 – 199	Plain carbon steels
	The second and third digits denote the manganese content
200 – 240	Free-cutting carbon steel equivalents of 000 – 199
	The 2nd and 3rd digits indicate the sulphur content
300 – 499	Stainless and valve steels
500 – 999	Other alloy steels

Table 1.5 The range of numbers in the British Standard used to define various types of steel.

Plain carbon steels					
BS970	070M20	080M30	080M40	150M36	080M50
EN number	EN3	EN5	EN8	EN15	EN43A
Free-cutting steels					
BS970	220M07	240M07	212M44	216M36	
EN numbers	EN1A	EN1B	EN8M	EN15AM	
Alloy steels					
BS970	526M60	503M40	653M31	659M15	817M40
Content	¾% Cr	1% Ni	3% NiCr	4% NiCr	1.5% NiCrMo
EN number	EN11	EN12	EN23	EN39A	EN24T
Stainless steels					
BS970	410S21	416S37	302S25	303S21	304S15
Content	13% Cr	13% Cr	18%Cr8%Ni	18%Cr8%Ni	18%Cr8%Ni
EN number	EN56A	EN56C	EN58A	EN58M	EN58A

Table 1.6 Acceptable replacements for some of the steels specified in the old EN numbers.

example, 50 mean 0.50% carbon. If the carbon content exceeds 1.0%, the last two digits are always 99.

055M25 is a typical example of BS 970 designations. It is a plain carbon steel, supplied with specified mechanical properties, having 0.25% carbon and 0.55% manganese. Other examples include 215A25, which is a free-cutting steel supplied against chemical analysis, with 0.15% sulphur and 0.25% carbon. 503H40 is an alloy steel of 0.4% carbon content and with a particular ability to be hardened.

It is important to remember that high carbon tool steels are not covered by BS970. Silver steel is specified in BS 1407 while BS 1499 provides a wider range of specifications for stainless steels.

Where ultimate tensile strength is the major requirement, in normalised or hot-rolled condition, Table 1.7 shows the materials in order of increasing strength.

Mild steel

Mild steel is easily the most widely used form of steel and is available as black steel and bright-drawn mild steel (BDMS) or bright mild steel (BMS). Mild steel sheet is widely used to make items like the bodies of locomotives and traction engines, drip trays and steel boxes. Old car bodies and office furniture provide a useful source of scrap mild steel.

Normalising mild steel
Normalising ensures a uniform, unstressed internal structure of steel. It makes high-carbon steels soft and much easier to machine. If steel is cold-worked, the structure of the metal is distorted and there are unequal stresses in the material, which may cause distortion. Steel can be normalised by slowly heating it to just above the upper critical point and allowing it to cool in draught-free conditions at room temperature. For mild steel (0.3% carbon) this normalising temperature is approximately 800°C (bright red).

Black steel
Raw steel is manufactured in large billets which are worked to the required size and cross-section, usually when the material is hot. This results in a rather poor surface finish with a characteristic black scale.

UTS N/mm²	BS No.	Alloy elements
430	070M20	0.2% carbon, 0.7% manganese
460	080M30	0.3% carbon, 0.8% manganese
500	070M26	0.26% carbon, 0.7% manganese
525	120M28	0.28% carbon, 1.2% manganese
550	150M28	0.28% carbon, 1.5% manganese
620	080M46	0.46% carbon, 0.8% manganese
700	070M55	0.55% carbon, 0.7% manganese
620 –770	080M40	4% medium carbon steel
	503M40	4% carbon, 1% nickel
700 – 850	150M36	3.6% carbon, 1.5% manganese
	605M36	3.6% carbon, 1.5% manganese molybdenum
770 – 930	708M40	4% carbon, 1% chromium molybdenum
850 – 1000	630M40	4% carbon, 1% chromium
	709M40	4% carbon, 1.5% chromium molybdenum
1000 – 1150	817M40	4% carbon, 1% nickel chromium molybdenum
1080 – 1240	826M31	3.1% carbon, 2.5% nickel chromium molybdenum
1150 – 1400	826M40	4% carbon, 2.5% nickel chromium molybdenum
1540	835M30	3% carbon, 4% nickel chromium molybdenum

Table 1.7 The specification of a range of alloy steels of increasing ultimate tensile strength.

The advantage of this material is that it is comparatively free of internal stress. It is available from most model engineering suppliers but needs machining all over to get a smooth finish.

Bright-drawn or bright mild steel
BDMS and BMS have a shiny, scale-free surface produced by cold-drawing to produce the required section. Cold working stresses the steel, increasing its tensile strength while significantly reducing its ductility. Thus it needs heat treatment before cold bending it to avoid over stressing or fracturing the material.

The stresses locked in can also cause distortion if removing significant quantities of metal or making large holes. Thus stress should always be relieved and it is therefore not ideal for making complex parts. Round or hexagonal BDMS or BMS does not normally require stress relief if being turned, since this process sym-metrically removes metal. BDMS or BMS are widely available in sheets of varying thickness and as round, rectangular, square and hexagonal bars. The material is ideal if a clean surface finish is required but an accurate size is not important. To avoid problems when machining to a specific size or cold bending, it is better to use black mild steel.

Precision ground mild steel (PGMS)
PGMS is readily available as precisely sized, circular mild steel rods, normally 6mm – 40mm diameter. It is perfect for making axles and crank pins and is preferable to silver steel for load carrying purposes.

Free-cutting steel
Mild steel easily machines to a good finish with long, spiral curls of swarf. Free-cutting mild steel, containing small amounts of phosphorus and sulphur, results in the material coming off as small chips

Figure 1.7 A small water bucket made from galvanised steel.

and makes it easier to produce a smooth machined surface. Use a side rake of 15° for BDMS or BMS but 20° to 25° for free-cutting mild steel, and a speed of 25 to 30m/min.

Hand-working issues
Mild steel can be worked fairly easily using normal metalworking techniques. It is significantly harder than copper or brass to form into beaten shapes and flanges, usually needing a steel former. However, it will work in this way and is much stronger than most other metals.

Joining
Mild steel is quite easy to weld but, with thin sheet, distortion can be a problem. Brazing or silver soldering are even easier techniques to apply. Epoxy adhesives are suitable for some joining applications and, where the fit of two pieces supports the join, anaerobic adhesives are an excellent solution.

Corrosion
BDMS and BMS rust much more rapidly than black steel, where the oxide coating provides some protection. Mild steel will rust even in a dry, warm atmosphere, unless coated with oil or grease. Rusting takes place particularly quickly along the line of any welded joint.

It is, therefore, essential to protect anything made of mild steel. The alternatives are:

- Painting
- Plastic coating
- Galvanising

Galvanised steel
Galvanising mild steel sheet provides a protective layer of zinc which stops any rusting more effectively than tinplate. The material resembles zinc with a mottled finish. Galvanised steel must not be heated above 419°C, the melting point of zinc, making annealing, silver soldering, brazing and welding impracticable.

Galvanised steel can be riveted and soft-soldered but cut edges need protecting and heavily scribed lines should be avoided for the same reason. Cold working galvanised sheet cannot be carried out for long as, once it is work-hardened, it cannot be annealed without melting off the zinc. This spoils the material and the zinc fumes are a health hazard.

Galvanised steel is an alternative to mild steel sheet for many applications and gives greater rust protection while avoiding the need for painting. It is good for making water cans and funnels and in its corrugated form may be used in the construction of a home workshop.

Galvanised sheet is widely available from 0.7mm to 2mm thick. It is stocked by most model engineering suppliers and some engineering companies will sell off-cuts. Scrap items that may be used as a source include old cold water tanks and tin baths. Small sheets, about 600mm square but plastic coated brown or black on one side are also available.

Figure 1.8 Locomotive frames are usually fabricated from gauge plate, wheels from cast iron.

Carbon tool steels.

Carbon tool steel contains 0.7% – 1.5% carbon, almost always includes manganese and also one or more of the following; chromium, molybdenum, nickel and vanadium. High speed tool steel usually includes tungsten and cobalt.

High-carbon steel

As mentioned above, steels with more than 0.5% carbon are classified as high-carbon steels. The two common forms of high-carbon steel are silver steel and gauge plate. Both come in a soft condition and their degree of hardness is easily varied by heat treatment.

Silver steel

Silver steel has wide applications and is made in large quantities. It is a high-carbon steel suitable for hardening and ideal for making cutting tools, punches and scribers. Small amounts of chromium included in silver steel minimise distortion on heat treatment. It is commonly supplied in 330mm lengths of rod accurately ground to within 0.00635mm and manufactured by the firm of P. Stubs. Stamped 'STUBS' at one end distinguishes this material from other bright steels.

Stubs silver steel contains 1.1 – 1.2% carbon and small amounts of chromium, manganese and silicon. It has a slightly higher tensile strength than mild steel but is much less ductile. It is more expensive than mild steel, harder to machine and no better wearing.

Silver steel is very difficult to machine to a smooth surface finish and a free-cutting carbon steel is becoming available from some suppliers, which is equally easy to harden. This is not available in such a wide range of sizes as silver steel but offers a big advantage in terms of ease of machining. It is also cheaper than the ground-finish Stubs silver steel.

When machining silver steel with an HSS tool, use a cutting angle of 8° to 10° and a speed of 18m/min. It can be shaped using basic tools, hardened and tempered to avoid its inherent brittleness. Silver steel should not be used when hardened for load-bearing applications.

Silver steel is frequently recommended for use when making crank pins due to the accuracy with which it is ground to size during manufacture. However, it is not as easy to machine as mild steel with no better wearing properties. A harder, wear-resisting surface may be obtained by case-hardening mild steel. This produces a hard surface with a softer, more-resilient core, whereas hardened silver steel is brittle right through and it thus may fail in service.

13

HSS	Hardness	Carbon	Chromium	Molybdenum	Tungsten	Vanadium	Cobalt
BM1	823	c.0.8%	c.4%	c.8.5%	c.1.5%	c.1%	<1%
BM2	836	0.87%	4%	c.5%	c.2%	c.2%	<1%
BT1	823	0.75%	4%	<0.7%	c.18%	c.1%	<1%

Table 1.8 Constituents of some BS 4659 high speed steels (HSS).   c. = approximately

Gauge plate

Gauge plate or ground flat stock is a high-carbon steel available in bars, 500mm long, of rectangular cross-section which are accurately ground to thickness. It usually contains around 1% carbon and small amounts of chromium, manganese, tungsten and vanadium.

Gauge plate is supplied in a soft state but may be hardened after machining to size. It is suitable for making cutting and form tools. Gauge plate is as much as ten times as expensive as mild steel.

High speed steel (HSS)

High speed steel is the most popular metal for making home workshop lathe cutting

Figure 1.9 A quality spring is essential to the operation of this governor.

tools. It remains hard during high speed machining. Its carbon content is up to 1.5% and other carbide-forming elements such as chromium, molybdenum, tungsten and vanadium are usually added.

The high carbon content results in a hard martensitic structure and the carbides provide additional abrasion resistance when using the steel for cutting. High speed steels typically keep their hardness to at least 500°C. BS 4659 specifies the various types of HSS. The numbering classification is the same as the AISI system except that the British numbers all have a 'B' added to the start. The most popular grades are shown in Table 1.8.

Spring steel

Spring steel is the term for any steel used to make springs. Most springs are made of steel but, when corrosion resistance or electrical conductivity are important, brass, bronze, nickel silver or phosphor bronze are alternatives.

Carbon steel with 0.50 – 1.0% carbon is ideal but needs to have a low content of sulphur and phosphorus. Piano wire is a high grade, uniform steel of this type and is widely employed for making small spiral springs.

Steel for watch mainsprings has 1.15% carbon and 0.15 – 0.25% manganese. This steel is rolled hard to give an elastic limit above 2,000N/mm².

Silicon spring steels have both high strength and impact resistance. These steels usually contain around 0.4% carbon, 0.75 – 2% silicon, and 0.95% manganese. The elastic limit of these steels is from

700 – 2,000N/mm^2, depending on the drawing temperature, with hardness 250 to 600 Brinell.

Vanadium and chrome vanadium steels are also employed for heavy duty springs. The addition of chromium or other elements improves their physical properties.

Wire for making coil springs contains from 0.50 to 1.20% carbon and 0.028% sulphur. Cold working is used to harden the wire and raise its tensile strength from around 1,000N/mm^2 to an ultimate strength of 2,750N/mm^2. The best grades of wire are referred to as piano wire.

For applications where resistance to high temperatures is needed, stainless and high-alloy steel springs are used with the alloying element carefully controlled.

Figure 1.10 Quality spanners are usually made from chrome vanadium alloy steel.

Alloy steels
High alloy, stainless steels are made by melting mild steel in an electric arc furnace and adding large percentages of alloying elements; typically copper, manganese, molybdenum, nickel, silicon, titanium or tungsten. Low alloy steels usually have a total of less than 5% of these elements.

Stainless steel
Just before the First World War, work on improving steels used to make rifle barrels resulted in the development of the first stainless steel, but until the 1970s, the material was still very expensive and only produced in quantities of around 10 tonnes at a time. By alloying iron with chromium, a thin protective layer is formed which resists corrosion. The chromium produces a bright, silver-coloured alloy and traditionally, when the chromium exceeds 12%, the material is known as stainless steel. The chromium oxide skin effectively prevents further chemical action and virtually eliminates rusting, but hardens the material making most stainless steels difficult to machine.

In the 1920s and 1930s, much further developmental work on stainless steels resulted in most of the popular alloys in use today. This was achieved by adding other elements, mainly nickel and carbon, to improve the characteristics of the steels. Up to 22% nickel may be used with 8 – 25% chromium. Depending on

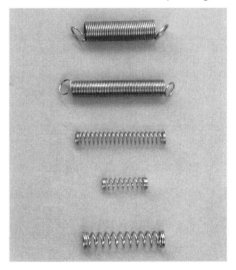

Figure 1.11 Making quality springs requires careful selection of the correct type of steel.

AISI	302	303	304	310	316
BS970	302S25	303S21	304S15	310S24	316S33
Old EN number	EN58A	EN58M	EN58A		
Key content	18% Cr	18% Cr	18%Cr	25% Cr	18% Cr
	8% Ni	9% Ni	9%Ni	3% Mo	0.15% S
Free cutting	No	Yes	No	No	Yes
Corrosion properties	Excellent	Good	Good	Exceptional	Excellent

AISI	410	416	
BS970	410S21	416S37	
Old EN number	EN56A	EN56C	
Key content	12% Cr	12% Cr 0.15% S	
Free cutting	No	Yes	

Table 1.9 The properties of some popular AISI stainless steels.

the amount of nickel, slow cooling or annealing can leave the steel in different states of hardness. Many stainless steels are non-magnetic or only mildly magnetic. The latter may require annealing to become non-magnetic since cold working can induce magnetism.

The carbon content is usually kept well below 1% and is an essential constituent of heat-treatable stainless steel. Small percentages of aluminium, manganese, molybdenum, nitrogen, phosphorus, selenium, silicon, sulphur and titanium may also be included.

Free-cutting alloys contain small amounts of sulphur, typically 0.3%. A free-cutting non-magnetic stainless steel, 303S21, is similar to the well known 302S25 (18/8) stainless steel with 17 – 19% chromium, 8 – 11% nickel, 1 – 2% silicon and manganese and 0.12% carbon. When machining stainless steel with HSS tools, a cutting angle of 8° – 10° is recommended at a speed of 18m/min.

However, the sulphur in free-cutting 303 results in a reduction of its corrosion properties compared with 'standard' 304. Corrosion resistance is improved in 303Se, while maintaining the free-cutting properties, by replacing the sulphur with selenium, while retaining the same content of chromium and nickel.

Model engineers' suppliers normally stock stainless steel tubes up to about 12mm diameter and circular rods up to 25mm. A range of rectangular sections is also useful for superheater return bends and for making fire grates. Ground rods are available from some sources.

While Britain and Europe, and most other industrial nations, have their own standards for stainless steels, the American AISI numbering system is in almost universal use at present.

Non-shrinking oil-hardened steel
This is a group of alloy steels which do not easily distort when heat treated. They usually contain 1 – 1.75% manganese and may include other alloying elements, particularly chromium. The amount of carbon is the same as in similar grades of tool steel. These steels are oil hardened, thus their name, but do not have the tough core of ordinary tool steel. They are normally used to make items such as dies and gauges where accurate size is essential.

16

Figure 1.12 Stainless steel is useful for making jet engine burners as well as steam locomotive superheaters.

Heat treating steel

The carbon contained in steel produces iron carbide (cementite). This makes the steel harder and tougher as the quantity of carbon increases up to about 1.5%. With 0.87% carbon, the material is known as eutectoid steel and contains 13% thin grains of cementite with 87% slender particles of ferrite. This combination is called pearlite. If eutectoid steel is heated to 700°C, the pearlite changes as the cementite and ferrite merge to form a solid, non-magnetic solution of carbon in iron, called austenite.

Steels containing different amounts of carbon experience a two-stage change. At 700°C (the lower critical point) the structure starts to alter, but the change to austenite takes time and is not complete until the steel reaches and is held above the upper critical point for some time.

If cooled slowly, the austenite reverts to pearlite. Rapid cooling stops this reversion and creates glass-hard martensite; the faster the cooling, the greater the amount of martensite and the harder the resultant steel. However, the greater degree of hardness also results in an extremely brittle material.

Hardening temperatures vary with the amount of carbon. For silver steel, with 1.2% carbon, the upper critical point is 800°C. For other steels the critical point depends on what other elements have been included. The manufacturer may quote a temperature but otherwise try an upper critical point of 810 – 840°C.

Rate of heating: Very gradual.

Temperature: 800 – 850°C (cherry to bright red) for silver steel or gauge plate.

Soaking: 25 minutes per centimetre of thickness.

17

Figure 1.13 The shaft of this lathe centre height jig is made from hardened silver steel.

Figure 1.14. Different qualities of steel are needed for the various components of an elevated railway track.

Quenching: In water preferably with100g of salt per litre of water at 20 – 25°C. Agitate to remove bubbles of steam. For toughness rather than hardness and to avoid distortion, quench in clean 20SAE viscosity engine oil. This is inclined briefly to catch fire but special quenching oils overcome this problem.

Tempering: Heat slowly, 20 minutes per centimetre of thickness.

Annealing: Heat slowly to just above 800°C, hold for 25 minutes per centimetre of thickness and very slowly cool.

Case hardening

Case hardening produces a hard, wear-resistant surface skin, up to 1.5mm thick, on a black or bright-drawn mild steel component while still retaining the toughness of a low carbon inner core. This is achieved by diffusing carbon into the surface layers of low carbon steel.

To create the hardened skin, heat the steel item to 925°C (a bright orange-red) and dip in a tray of case-hardening compound (carburiser). This powder melts onto the hot component, sticking to its surface. Create a really good coating by

Temp °C	Temper colour	Uses
210	Pale yellow	Turning tools for brass
250	Pale straw	Turning tools for steel, taps and dies
255	Dark straw	Milling cutters
265	Yellow-brown	Routing cutters
270	Brown-red	Wood-boring tools
275	Brown-purple	Twist drills
280	Light purple	Axes
290	Purple	Bone and ivory saws
295	Dark purple	Punches, cold chisels
300	Full blue	Screwdrivers
320	Dark blue	Springs

Table 1.10 The degree of temper alters the hardness of steel and its application to many tasks.

successively heating and dipping until the item is adequately coated. Then reheat to 925°C and quench in water. Finally remove any remaining carburiser.

In the home workshop, case hardening may be carried out using granular charcoal but is normally done using a carburising powder which also contains sodium or barium carbonate to improve the process.

Conclusion

Both iron and steel are widely available and their use fundamental to most areas of model engineering. However, it should be clear that, by making a careful choice of the right type of alloy, it is possible to ensure that the one selected is the one best suited to the particular task in hand.

CHAPTER 2

Aluminium and copper

Non-ferrous metals and their alloys are generally less stiff and strong than ferrous metals and less suitable for welding. They do, however, enjoy several advantages over ferrous ones.

- Lower density allowing production of lightweight components.
- Easier cold working because of better ductility.
- Better resistance to corrosion without special coatings.
- Both higher electrical and thermal conductivity.
- Casting at lower temperatures.
- A wider range of natural colours.

Aluminium

Aluminium is the most widely occurring metal in the Earth's crust and, after iron, is the next most important metal, valued for its lightweight properties. It is refined from bauxite, aluminium oxide, by electrolysis at high temperatures; a process requiring prolific quantities of electricity. It is thus normal to find aluminium produced in areas where there are abundant quantities of low cost hydro-electric power. Producing a kilogram of aluminium consumes some 400g of carbon, mainly

in the form of anodes, and requires more than 13kWh of electricity. No wonder recycling of aluminium is so popular!

This silvery-grey coloured, non-magnetic metal is recognised as one of the lightest metals and its alloys are therefore widely used by the aerospace industry. Its density, at 2.7g/cc, is roughly one-third of the figures for copper and steel. It is very corrosion resistant as it rapidly forms a thin surface oxide layer when exposed to air. This layer then protects the metal from further corrosion. It is also a good thermal and electrical conductor. This last characteristic results in aluminium often being used instead of copper for electrical conductors, particularly where weight is an issue. Although it has only two-thirds the conductivity of copper, it is better on a weight-for-weight basis. Its main disadvantage is its relative weakness; roughly one-third as strong as steel. Tensile strength figures are $82N/mm^2$ for cast aluminium and $165N/mm^2$ for cold rolled material.

Pure aluminium is a soft, very ductile metal that is virtually useless in this raw state, though work-hardening improves its strength as well as hardness, at the same time reducing its ductility. It melts at 658.7°C. It is used to make kitchen foil (around 0.015mm thick) and other foils, as well as reflectors to fit behind radiators and mirrors for telescopes. It has very little application in the home workshop.

British and US standards for aluminium and its non-heat treatable alloys are similar and some examples are shown in Table 2.1. In the British Standard, the letter H is followed by a number which indicates the degree of work-hardening. In the American one, the letter indicates strain hardened, while the first number shows the process used to attain the temper and the second the degree of hardness.

Aluminium powder
Widely used as a pigment in 'silver' paints, powdered aluminium is also available as an additive which can be mixed with resin to make 'metallic' castings. Note, however, that this powder is inflammable and burns with an intense heat.

Aluminium alloys
For the vast majority of practical uses, there is a wide range of engineering alloys made from aluminium with one or more of the following elements added in various proportions – copper, magnesium, manganese and silicon. Compared to pure aluminium, these alloys improve both strength and machining properties. The alloys can all be cast, drawn, extruded, machined, pressed, rolled and welded. Some can be heat treated to increase strength and the best are as strong as mild steel but only one-third of the weight.

The best-known aluminium alloy is duralumin or dural, first produced in Düren

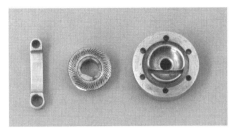

Figure 2.1 Aluminium con rod, prop driver and cylinder head for a model aero engine.

in Germany early in the twentieth century; thus the name. It contains 4 – 5% copper and less than 1% each of silicon, iron, manganese, magnesium and zinc. Dural is about twice as strong as aluminium (tensile strength 193N/mm^2) and roughly two-thirds the strength of steel. Similar alloys contain only 0.1% of copper, but greater quantities of magnesium: 0.5 – 5%.

Extruded angles, tees, U-shapes and drawn or extruded tubes are normally only available in high magnesium content alloys. Dural is available as extruded rounds, hexagons and flats from most metal suppliers. Sheet, plate and strip are supplied in 99% pure aluminium, magnesium-rich alloys or as the copper-rich dural.

Already mentioned, aluminium provides good corrosion resistance as exposure to air quickly produces a tough, thin oxide skin, which prevents further corrosion. This skin is only a few millionths of a millimetre thick. Anodising is a protective method which enables this skin to be thickened to around 0.025mm by chemical or electrolytic action and suitable solutions can be found in Chapter 9. Both

British Standard	American Standard	Condition of material
M	F	As manufactured
O	O	Annealed/soft
H4	Hx4	Half work-hardened
H8	Hx8	Fully work-hardened

Table 2.1 British and US terminology for hardness of aluminium.

Series	Main alloying element
1000	Aluminium over 99% pure
2000	Copper
3000	Manganese
4000	Silicon
5000	Magnesium
6000	Magnesium and silicon
7000	Zinc
8000	Lithium and other elements

Table 2.2 Classification of aluminium alloys.

Figure 2.2 Aluminium extrusions are suitable for a wide range of applications.

methods increase resistance to corrosion and hardness, also adding colour. Alloying itself reduces oxide formation, so that most aluminium alloys exhibit a good level of natural corrosion resistance, though they are attacked by salt water.

Wrought aluminium alloys, available as bar, extrusions, foil, forgings, tubes and wire, are classified by a four digit number, depending on their main alloying element. Table 2.2 shows this and a final letter indicates the type of heat treatment.

Aluminium work-hardens and is thus available with different degrees of temper. Some aluminium alloys, particularly those of aluminium and copper, are also susceptible to age hardening but can be softened by heat treatment, though they will then reharden with time. Aluminium and most of its alloys are easy to cold work, being quite malleable after annealing. Many of them harden, or stiffen, quite rapidly with time as well as the more usual work-hardening. However, even in its hard state, aluminium is still a relatively soft metal. Typical grades are:

HE 9 Soft grade – easy to bend.

HE 15 High tensile, free-cutting alloy.

HE 30 Medium tensile, free cutting, general-purpose alloy.

Joining

Aluminium has a relatively low melting point; around 650°C. Although modern solders have reduced the difficulty of this method of joining aluminium and made it straightforward for the amateur, rivets, nuts and bolts and adhesives are still often used for joining the material. Aluminium pop rivets can be especially useful when working with aluminium. Epoxy adhesives are worth considering for some jointing applications.

Availability and uses

Aluminium, in all its forms, is a fairly easy metal to obtain from scrap components. In sheet form it can be found in all sorts of containers, cooking utensils, camping equipment, commercial vehicle and some car body work. Aluminium sheet can be obtained cheaply from all these items. Sports equipment, model railway controller cases, model and full-size aircraft can all have parts made from it.

New material is easy to obtain. Offcuts of around 300mm square of 1mm to 2mm thickness are available at many model shows. Stores selling motor cycle or car spares and building materials also often sell aluminium sheet offcuts. This is in addition to the more usual metal suppliers. Aluminium is slightly more expensive than mild steel, size for size.

Aluminium alloys are used where their light weight is needed. A typical example

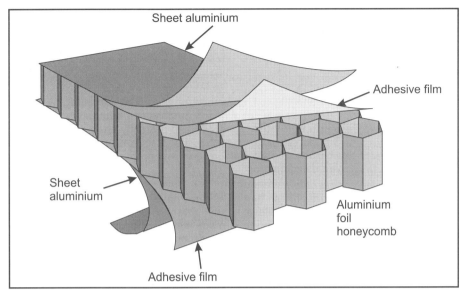

Figure 2.3 Aluminium honeycomb involves a surprisingly complex construction.

is the parts for model aero engines. Where the highest strength is not needed, these alloys are ideal for casting due to their comparatively low melting temperature and ease of machining. Aluminium sheet is also useful for making boxes and containers for electrical and electronic items. It may also be used to make heat sinks for solid-state power supplies. Aluminium honeycomb structures, developed for the aerospace industry, are now widely available in a range of sizes of exceptional strength-to-weight ratios.

Avoid mixing aluminium and steel as, when damp, they have a very corrosive effect on each other. Never repair steel body work with aluminium patches.

Heat treatment
As already mentioned, dural age-hardens at room temperature. Thus it is normally hard and cannot be bent through more than a small angle without fracturing.

Sheet dural needs to be annealed before trying to make a significant bend.

Since dural melts at about 650°C it is easy to ruin any item being annealed by overheating, so the process requires care. Before heating, rub the surface of the metal with a piece of ordinary soap. Evenly heat the material until the soap turns black, which occurs at the annealing temperature of 400°C. The work should then be quenched in water at 15°C to 20°C making it fully soft. Age hardening at room temperature causes a doubling in hardness over the next four to five days and this hardness can be further increased by around a third by reheating to 175°C, a process known as precipitation treatment. Any bends should therefore be done as soon as possible after annealing.

The British and American standards for alloys that are heat treatable are rather different and some examples are found

British Standard	American Standard	Condition of material
M		As manufactured
O		Annealed/soft
TB		Solution treated, quenched and naturally aged
TB7		Solution treated and stabilised (cast metals)
TD		Solution treated, quenched, cold-worked and naturally aged
TE		Cooled from a hot-working process and naturally aged
TF		Solution treated, quenched and naturally aged
TF7		Solution treated, quenched and stabilised
TH		Solution treated, cold-worked and naturally aged
	T2	Annealed casting
	T3	Solution treated, quenched, cold-worked and naturally aged
	T4	Solution treated and naturally aged
	T5	Artificially aged
	T6	Solution treated and artificially aged
	T8	Solution treated, work-hardened and artificially aged

Table 2.3 Examples of the hardness of aluminium alloys to British and American standards.

in Table 2.3. In the British Standard, the letter T is followed by a second letter that indicates the form of treatment. In America, the letter is followed by a single number indicating the form of treatment.

Casting

Aluminium casting alloys mainly contain some or all of the following elements: copper, magnesium and silicon. They may also include a small amount of other metals such as manganese, nickel, titanium and zinc. Aluminium alloy castings may be made in sand moulds and, though not suitable for highly-stressed applications, are appropriate for a great number of modelling requirements.

When making castings, aluminium alloys with reasonably high levels of silicon give greater fluidity to the molten alloy. The thinner the sections of the casting the greater the need for more silicon. However, the abrasive nature of silicon and the formation of hard compounds within the alloy does increase the difficulty of machining the final casting.

Various alloys have different names, depending on the country and the progress of time. A popular casting alloy, known in the UK as LM24 with around 8% silicon and 3% copper, is now referred to under ISO specifications as AlSi8Cu3Fe, the last two letters indicating that it also contains a trace of iron. With its low melting point, aluminium is suitable for casting in the home workshop.

Machining

Aluminium is obtainable in a range of qualities and degrees of hardness. It is a very free-cutting material that generates plenty of heat when it is machined. It is easy to obtain a fine finish but, because it is a soft metal, it is easily damaged when tightening it in a chuck or clamping it in place on a table or in a vice. It is difficult to recommend a particular side rake cutting angle for HSS tools when used with aluminium alloys, but a figure from 25° to 40° is a good starting point and a relatively high cutting speed of 90m/min. Swarf formation depends on

24

Type	Composition %	Condition	Tensile strength N/mm²	Elong-ation %	Typical uses
Wrought	Al 98.8, Mn 1.2.	Soft	110	34	Domestic,
		Hard	200	4	automobile
	Al 94.8, Mg 4.5, Mn 0.7.	Soft	315	15	Corrosion-
		Half hard	345	8	resistant parts
Cast	Al 91.6, Si 5, Cu 3, Mn 0.4.	Sand cast	140	2	General-purpose castings
	Al 88.5, Si 11.5.	Sand cast	160	5	Vehicle castings
	Al 92.2, Cu 4, Ni 2, Mg 1.5, Si 0.3.	Cast & heat treated	290	2	Pistons, cylinder heads

Table 2.4 Some of the properties and uses of aluminium alloys.

the grade of material and varies from long rolled chips to fine powder. A problem is the build-up of waste material on the cutting tool, particularly between the teeth of milling cutters. A good supply of lubricant minimises this but still requires regular clearing of any build-up on the tool.

Lubricating
When machining aluminium and its alloys, it is important to employ plenty of suitable lubricant to get a fine finish. Paraffin is highly recommended for this purpose.

Hand-working issues
The main issue when working aluminium is how to hold the work piece without marking the soft metal. Clogging of saw blades, drill bits and files also means that they need frequent cleaning.

Aluminium brass and bronze
These alloys have rather misleading names. Aluminium brass is a copper/zinc alloy with only a very small amount of aluminium, while aluminium bronze is a copper/aluminium alloy with up to 10% aluminium. These alloys are listed under brass on page 29 and bronze on page 34.

Copper

Copper was one of the first metals used by man and is even mentioned in the Old Testament of the Bible. The major source of copper is the ore, pyrites, containing around one-third copper. After refining, the copper is separated in a blast furnace to produce relatively pure metal. Further refining, such as electrolysis, produces commercial grade copper.

This very pure electrolytic copper is used to prepare copper alloys. It weighs

Figure 2.4 A seamless copper tube cut to length with discs ready for forming into end flanges. Figure 2.5 overleaf shows the end result.

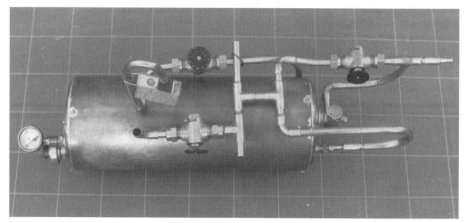

Figure 2.5 A compressed air storage tank made from copper tube and sheet.

8.9g/cc and in its cast form has a tensile strength of around 125N/mm² though this increases to 275N/mm² for cold-drawn copper.

Pure copper is widely used but fairly expensive. It is an excellent conductor of heat and electricity and, for this reason alone, is widely used. It is readily ductile, malleable and can be drawn to produce fine wire, forged, pressed or spun into complex shapes without cracking. It is relatively weak, though its strength and hardness increase with working. It can be joined by soldering or brazing and melts at around 1083°C. It is pleasant to bend or shape as it is very soft and pliable. Its red/brown colour and ability to polish well make it a popular choice for decorative work.

Copper resists atmospheric corrosion well since, when exposed to air, it grows a protective coating of its green oxide. This is seen on the roofs of many churches and public buildings. It is this corrosion resistance that makes copper useful for many applications but some chemicals, including atmospheric salt, attack copper.

Hand-working copper
Hand-working, such as filing and sawing is difficult as copper tends to tear and clog tools. Clogging of files can be reduced by rubbing chalk into the tool before work starts. However a file will still need frequent cleaning. Copper tends to work-harden fairly quickly and will need to be softened regularly when forming, for example, the dished end to a boiler.

Machining and lubricating
Copper can be machined at the same speed as BMS; around 25 to 30m/min. A tool side rake angle of 20° to 25° is recommended. The same problems of splitting and clogging occur when drilling or machining copper but both these processes are eased by the application of plenty of oil.

Heating
Because of its good conductivity, brazing and soldering copper require a lot more heating than do other metals. Heat applied at one point is rapidly diffused through the copper. Thus plenty of pre-heating is needed for a component of

26

any significant size. However, overheating copper for long periods at silver soldering temperatures weakens the metal making it less shock resistant. Fortunately this is not so at annealing temperatures.

Work-hardening and annealing
Copper is very malleable and ductile but suffers from work-hardening. It is easy to anneal copper by raising it to dull red heat, around 600°C, and leaving it slowly to cool. Rapid cooling in clean water at room temperature helps remove any scale which forms and is satisfactory unless there is a risk of distortion. Annealing occurs rapidly so do not overheat the metal. Copper quickly hardens when worked and may fracture if work continues, so it must regularly be softened by annealing.

Degrees of temper
Hot-working copper avoids work-hardening allowing it to be produced in a soft condition. This is available commercially only in a limited range of small tubes and sheets due to its susceptibility to damage.

Copper, cold rolled to its final thickness to produce commercial sheets, is work-hardened by the rolling process. Depending upon the amount of cold working, the copper may be anywhere between soft and fully hard. The degrees of hardness or temper, available from most metal stockists, are soft, quarter, half and fully hard. Half hard is common and a good compromise for most requirements. It is hard enough to allow easy handling, marking and cutting but readily softened by annealing.

Availability and uses
The main model engineering uses of copper are for boilers and pipe work, as its corrosion resistance, ductile nature and ease of soldering make it the perfect material. Two of the more popular types are:

C101	Hard drawn copper rod.
C109	Free-machining copper which contains tellurium.

Copper is available in sheet, circular or rectangular bars and tube form. Copper sheet, 1200 x 600mm in size, is supplied by metal stockists in a wide range of standard thicknesses. Smaller pieces can be purchased from model engineering suppliers. Bars or tubes which have been drawn or extruded, without subsequent heat treatment, are hard but tubes are also available in a soft state. Soft tubes are normally supplied coiled; hard copper tubes straight. Tubes have either a specified bore or outside diameter and it is essential to know which when making a purchase. Model engineers' suppliers normally stock by outside diameter. Some copper strip is available in a soft condition, particularly if of small cross-section. To avoid damage during handling, sheet usually comes in either hard or an intermediate state between hard and soft.

A good source of copper sheet is scrap hot water cylinders, while central heating and domestic water pipes come in two popular diameters.

Enamel or resin-coated copper wire is commonly used for winding coils for transformers, generators, magnetos and electric motors. It is widely available in diameters from 0.18mm to 0.35mm.

Joining
Copper is easily soft- or hard-soldered, or brazed, and sheets can also readily be riveted with copper rivets, joined with a fold or even glued with epoxy.

Copper alloys
Copper is also important because of its wide use in alloys with aluminium, nickel, tin and zinc. Brass and bronze alloys come

Name	Constituents
Admiralty bronze	Copper 70%, tin 1%, zinc 29%
Admiralty gunmetal	Copper 88%, tin 10%, zinc 2%
Aluminium brass	Copper 77.5%, zinc 20.5%, aluminium 2%
Aluminium bronze	Copper/aluminium
Beryllium bronze	Copper/beryllium
Brass	Copper/zinc alloy
Bronze	Copper/tin
Cartridge brass	Copper 70%, zinc 30%
Cupro-nickel	Copper/nickel
Gunmetal	Casting bronze
Monel	Copper 33% nickel 67%
Muntz metal	Copper 60%, zinc 40%
Nickel silver	Copper/nickel/zinc
Phosphor bronze	Copper/tin/phosphorus
Silicon bronze	Copper/silicon

Table 2.5 The main constituents of the various copper alloys.

British Standard	US CDA	Type of alloy	Material	Uses
C	C1xx	Wrought	Copper	Electrical conductors
CZ	C2xx		Brass	Heat exchangers, low pressure boilers, tubing
	C3xx		Leaded brass	Bearings
	C4xx		Bronze	Castings
PB	C5xx		Phosphor bronze	Bearings, gears, springs
CA	C6xx		Aluminium bronze (In US copper/silicon & some copper/zinc alloys)	Light-duty gears, pressure, vessels, valves
NS	C7xx		Nickel silver (In US also cupronickel)	Springs, tubing and heat exchangers
CN			Cupronickel	Tubing and heat exchangers
CS			Copper/silicon	Valve stems
CB			Copper/beryllium	Springs
	C8xx	Cast	Copper, brass, manganese bronze, copper/zinc/silicon.	
	C9xx		Bronze, leaded bronze, copper/tin/nickel, nickel silver, copper/aluminium/iron, copper/nickel/iron.	

Table 2.6 The classification and uses of copper and its alloys.

with a wide range of different properties. They are harder and stronger than copper and have lower melting points. They are, with good reason, popular materials with model engineers.

Brass – copper/zinc alloy

Brass has a characteristic yellow colour and is the most widely used copper alloy. It polishes, solders and machines well and is slightly harder than copper. Brass alloys

Type	Condition	Tensile strength	Elongation	Hardness
Cartridge brass	Annealed	325	70%	65
	Hard	695	5%	185
Common brass	Annealed	340	55%	65
	Hard	725	4%	185
Muntz metal	Hot rolled	370	40%	75

Table 2.7 The mechanical properties of some types of brass.

are made from a mix of copper and zinc; their characteristics depending on the proportion of these two metals and whether other elements are added. Binary brass alloys contain only copper and zinc. Brasses contain other metals to improve one or more properties of these alloys. Most brass melts around 900°C – 950°C and has a density of about 8.4g/cc. The tensile strength of brass varies greatly, depending on its composition, from 200N/mm² for some annealed grades to over 600N/mm² for others with hard tempers.

Brass can also suffer from problems. Alloys containing a high percentage of brass can experience de-zincification making the material both weak and porous. Stress corrosion occurs when water condenses on brass which is under stress and the combination accelerates corrosion.

Brass containing less than 36% zinc is called alpha brass and is very ductile. Most sheet brass is of this type and can be cold-worked into complex shapes. Beta brass, with a zinc content above 46%, becomes more brittle the higher the percentage of zinc. It is harder and is mainly used as a brazing material.

Alpha/beta brass, with 36 – 46% zinc, contains both types of alloy. These brasses are harder and stronger than the alpha brasses and most bar stock is of this type, often with other elements added to improve strength or ease machining.

Standard brass contains 63% copper and is suitable for simple cold working.

Aluminium is added to brass to increase its strength. High-tensile brass contains 3% aluminium and just a little iron and manganese. Small traces of lead improve machining properties, but significant quantities weaken the alloy.

Gilding metal is a brass that contains 85% copper and is malleable, making it suitable for beaten work. A high copper content makes the brass simpler to form or press.

Brass takes a fine polish and is very resistant to corrosion, especially by sea water. It is widely used on boats. Acids attack it, especially the zinc content. Brass progressively breaks down at high temperatures and is unsuitable for boiler fittings except at the lowest operating pressures.

Muntz metal

This yellow brass alloy, named after its inventor, is made from 60% copper and

Figure 2.6 Brass rod is available in a huge range of shapes and sizes.

Name/number	Constituent %	Characteristics and typical applications
210 Gilding. 95%	95Cu, 5Zn	Excellent cold working; good hot working. Typical uses: jewellery base for gold plate, plaques.
230 Red brass. 85%	85Cu, 15Zn	Excellent cold and good hot forming. Typical uses: conduit, heat exchanger tubes, fasteners, plumbing pipe, radiator cores.
240 Low brass, 80%	80Cu, 20Zn	Excellent cold working. Typical uses: bellows, clock dials, flexible hose, pump lines.
260 Cartridge brass, 70% 268, 270 Yellow brass	70Cu, 30Zn 65Cu, 35Zn	Excellent cold working. Typical uses: fasteners, hinges, lamp fixtures, locks, pins, plumbing accessories, radiators, rivets.
443 – 445 Inhibited admiralty brass	71Cu, 28Zn, 1Sn	Excellent cold working for forming/bending Typical uses: condenser and heat exchanger tubes/plates.
280 Muntz metal	60.0Cu, 40.0Zn	Large nuts/bolts, brazing rod, heat exchanger/condenser tubes, hot forgings.
464 – 467 Naval brass	60Cu, 39.25Zn, 0.75Sn	Excellent hot working and hot forging. Typical uses: balls, bolts, condenser plates, marine hardware, nuts, propeller shafts, rivets, valve stems, welding rod.
667	70Cu, 28.8Zn, 2.8Mn, 1Sn	Excellent cold forming. Typical uses: bushes, gears, con-rods, shafts, wear plates.
687 Aluminium brass, arsenical	77.5Cu, 20.5Zn, 2Al, 0.1As	Excellent cold working for forming and bending. Typical uses: condenser, evaporator and heat exchanger tubes and plates, ferrules.
688	73.5Cu, 22.7Zn, 3.4Al, 0.4Co	Excellent hot and cold forming. Typical uses: contacts, drawn parts, relays, springs, switches.
694 Silicon red brass	81.5Cu, 14.5Zn, 4Si	Excellent hot forming for fabrication by forging, Typical uses: corrosion resistant/high strength valve stems.

Table 2.8 The name, composition and uses of various types of brass.

40% brass. It is useful for making tubes for heat exchangers and condensers and is also common as brazing rod.

Aluminium brass

This alloy is a copper/zinc alloy which contains 1 – 2% aluminium. It is normally

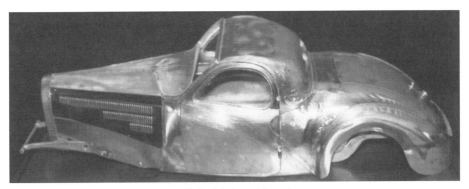

Figure 2.7 A Bugatti car body beautifully fabricated from brass.

used either as a casting alloy, which both flows and machines well, or as wrought material. Columbro™ aluminium brass is a corrosion-resistant alloy, available as round rod in sizes from 6mm to 30mm diameter with better performance and fabrication properties than most normal brass. In addition to excellent corrosion resistance, aluminium brass is readily worked and machined. It is lead-free and has a very low magnetic permeability. Uses include corrosion-resistant fittings and magnetically sensitive components.

Annealing
Like other metals, brass work hardens when bent and beaten into shape and may fracture if work continues. Frequent annealing is essential to soften it. The temperature required is 400°C to 600°C. Dull red or just below in subdued daylight is around the right temperature. Annealing only takes a short time so avoid excess heating. There is no need to quench brass but it helps to remove any scale which forms. It also tends to distort large sheets but, if this is not a problem, use clean water at 15°C to 20°C.

Overheating brass for long periods makes the metal weaker and less able to withstand shocks. This should not be a problem when annealing but may be at silver soldering temperatures.

Degrees of temper
Brass does not work-harden when hot so it can be produced in a soft condition but it is prone to damage. Soft tubes and sheet are, therefore, only available in a limited range of sizes. Depending upon the amount of cold rolling, brass may be anything from soft to completely hard but is usually supplied as soft, quarter, half or fully hard.

Figure 2.8 A small steam plant built largely from brass and aluminium.

31

Name/number	Composition %	Uses
220 Bronze 90%	Cu 90, Sn 10	Grillwork, marine hardware, screws, rivets
226 Jewellery 87.5%	Cu 87.5, Sn 12.5	Angles, base for gold plate, channels, chain, fasteners
675 Manganese bronze	Cu 58.5, Fe 1.4, Zn 39, Sn 1, Mn 0.1	Balls, clutch disks, pump rods, shafts, valve stems and bodies. Excellent hot workability
Admiralty gunmetal	Cu 88, Sn 10, Zn 2	Pumps & valves, particularly marine use
Phosphor bronze	Cu 88.5, Sn 11 P 0.5	Cast sticks. Bearings and bushes
Aluminium bronze	Cu 86, Al 9.5, Fe 2.5, Ni < 1, Mn < 1	Corrosion-resistant sand and die casting

Table 2.9 The composition and uses of a range of popular bronzes.

Half-hard brass is popular because it is hard enough to avoid transit damage but is satisfactory for most tasks and is readily softened by annealing.

Availability and uses
Size for size, brass is not as cheap as copper. In sheet form it may usually be obtained in 1200 x 600mm sheets in a range of the standard thicknesses. Brass is also available in smaller sheets, bar and square or circular tube form. Thick-walled tubes or hollow rod can also be obtained. In addition, equal and unequal angles, tee, U and half-round sections are available.

As bar and strip, scrap brass may often be obtained from redundant electrical equipment terminals or even plug pins but it is less easy to find in sheet form.

Brass sheet is used to make water tanks, body work for model locomotives, rolling stock and traction engines, decorative nameplates, many clocks, scientific instruments and etched model kits. Many chrome-plated items are made of brass.

Joining
Brass is an almost perfect metal for joining by soft soldering. This can be done with a soldering iron or by sweating pre-tinned components together. Alternatively, silver soldering, folded joints, ordinary riveting, bolting together or even gluing using epoxy are also straightforward.

Hand-working issues
Since copper forms the major constituent of most brasses, they also exhibit work-hardening, but it is only the alpha brasses (less than 36% of zinc) which are ductile and can readily be formed into complex shapes.

Machining
Brass is readily machined to a fine finish without any lubrication. Cutting speed should be around 90m/min with a tool cutting angle varying from zero for hard brass to only 5° for cartridge brass.

Bronze
Looking back in history it can be seen that the Bronze Age came after the Stone Age. Thus bronze is probably the metal which has been worked longer than any other. Despite this, it is far from the most popular metal with model engineers. It does, however, have some key applications,

Name	Condition	Tensile strength	Elongation	Hardness
Admiralty gunmetal	Sand cast	295N/mm²	16%	85 Brinell
Phosphor bronze	Sand cast	280N/mm²	15%	90 Brinell
Aluminium bronze	Cast	525N/mm²		115 Brinell

Table 2.10 The composition and uses of various bronzes.

which include use in the salt-laden marine environments.

Bronze is the generic name given to copper-tin alloys but commercial bronzes almost invariably also include some zinc. The contents of the various bronzes varies from 70 – 90% copper, 1 – 18% tin and 1 – 20% zinc with small amounts of other elements depending on the properties of the alloy. Because of the tin content, bronzes are generally stronger than brasses, with tensile strengths in the range 400 – 700N/mm². Density typically lies around 8.7g/cc.

Gunmetal
The bronze most likely to be used in the home workshop is gunmetal. This term is used for a group of bronzes that was originally used to make cannons and as a result cast well and are fairly strong. Gunmetal is corrosion resistant and widely used to make pump bodies, steam fittings and for castings that are subject to pressure or shock loads.

Rarely requiring much cleaning up and only essential machining, castings are widely available for model size boiler bushes, regulator bodies, steam fittings, valves and water pumps. Gunmetal is also popular for steam engine pistons and cylinders, though two different alloys are needed to minimise wear.

Continuously cast gunmetal or bronze is available as solid or hollow round bars which are ideal for turning into bushes or bearings. The term 'bearing bronze' is used for any bronze suitable for use as a bearing material. It particularly applies to

those incorporating significant amounts of lead for friction reduction. Bronze with around 30% lead is superior to Babbitt metal as a bearing material and is sometimes referred to as plastic bronze.

Phosphor bronze
Phosphor bronze contains from 10% – 14% tin with 0.1% – 0.3% phosphorus. This alloy is harder and stronger than gunmetal and is an ideal bearing material, particularly where loads are heavy. It is often used for commercial castings, particularly intricate ones, because of its fluidity when molten.

However, phosphor bronze is not the easiest material to machine. In the home workshop it is available in the form of drawn bars, for use as bearings, or for making steam fittings for model boilers, bearings, bushes, thrust washers, gears, and worm wheels. It has a density of 9g/cc and a tensile strength of 225N/mm². Phosphor bronze is also produced by continuous casting to nominal sizes and its machining qualities are excellent.

Rounds, tubes, squares, hexagons and flat bars are widely available in this useful material. Hard-drawn phosphor bronze wire can be bent quite easily to produce corrosion-free springs without subsequent heat treatment. Rolled strip is also useful for making springs and, because of its good electrical properties, spring contact electrical connections.

Colphos-90® is a wrought phosphor bronze which is more free cutting than conventional phosphor bronze; in fact as easy as free-cutting brass. It is ideal for complex machined components with close dimensional tolerances and high surface finish. Its mechanical properties are similar to wrought 5% phosphor bronze PB 102.

It is available in a range of round rod and hexagonal sections as well as in sheet form. It is corrosion and wear resistant with good thermal and electrical properties. Finely dispersed lead particles impart self-lubrication properties making the alloy ideal for applications like bearing bushes. Other uses include mechanical fasteners, pinions, self-lubricating gears and thrust washers.

LB4 is another free-cutting phosphor bronze. This is achieved by including lead in its content.

Figure 2.9 A typical complex-shaped bronze casting.

Trojan™

Columbia Metals' Trojan has a tensile strength above 800N/mm^2 and is an alloy of copper, nickel and silicon. It provides excellent mechanical properties while retaining all the physical attributes of other bronzes.

It is attractive for high-performance engine valve guides, bearing bushes and other high-duty applications. The alloy is beryllium-free and is a viable alternative to beryllium bronze. Trojan is available in round rod from 3mm to l00mm diameter.

Manganese bronze

A useful bronze variant, manganese bronze is basically an alpha-beta brass with 58% to 60% copper and 39% to 41% zinc, up to 2% manganese and up to 1% each of aluminium, iron and tin. This bronze is as strong as mild steel, easy to machine, very corrosion resistant and is perfect for bearings and steam fittings.

Aluminium bronze

Aluminium bronze is a copper/aluminium alloy (usually 5 – 10% aluminium) which is a very hard, wear-resistant alloy with excellent corrosion resistance and up to three times the strength of copper. It is used to make valves and valve guides as well as marine components.

Oilite sintered bronze

Bushes are often made by sintering or compression moulding bronze powder. This method of manufacture results in a porous material which is filled with oil for long-term lubrication. Ready-made bushes are manufactured in many sizes.

CHAPTER 3

Other non-ferrous metals

This chapter indicates the main uses of some of the less well-known metals, as well as carbon, often found in the home workshop only in alloys or specialist roles.

Antimony

Antimony is a blue/white metal often used in lead-based alloys, including some solders, to increase hardness and provide a smooth surface finish. As antimony-based alloys tend to expand on cooling they readily reproduce fine detail from a mould. Alloyed with copper, lead and tin, the resulting Babbitt metal is used as a bearing material for machinery.

Beryllium

The main ore of beryllium is called beryl. Synthetic beryl is still used for bearings in watches and scientific instruments.

Bismuth

This metal is unusual as it expands when it solidifies. It is found in casting alloys, particularly for small items to provide a sharp impression. It also improves the hardness and lowers the melting point of lead and tin alloys, making it a popular additive in fusible plugs and solders.

Cadmium

Cadmium used to be a popular additive to soft solders and fusible plugs, though its use in solders is slowly being phased out due to the resulting poisonous fumes. Cadmium is also used to harden and to increase the strength of copper and as a silver/white corrosion-resistant plating material for iron and steel.

Chromium

It is unlikely that any model will include a part made purely from chromium, but the metal is important as an electroplating finish on steel, zinc and brass, though its popularity for this purpose has declined from a high in the 1950s and 60s. As a plating material, it offers extreme hardness, a fine resistance to corrosion and can take a high polish.

By far its most important use is as an additive to many high performance steels;

Figure 3.1 Making a model jet engine requires extensive use of chromium-based alloys because of the high running temperature of many parts.

Figure 3.2 The exquisite chromium-plated engine and tank of a model BSA motor cycle.

notably stainless steels, which contain anything from 11 to 30% of this corrosion resisting metal. For those interested in building model gas turbines, the inconel and nimonic range of alloys has been developed from a basic content of 75% – 80% nickel and 15% – 20% chromium. More details of inconel and nimonic alloys are found on page 41.

Cobalt

The importance of cobalt lies in its use in cutting alloys and tool steels as well as its employment in magnetic alloys such as Alnico. Cobalt steels are rarer and more expensive than those containing nickel, making their use in model engineering unusual. Around a third of all cobalt mined is used to improve the magnetic properties of steel and is found in the magnets of many DC motors. It is also found in many alloy steels where high strength and corrosion resistance at high temperatures are important.

Lead

Best known for its weight and its use on church roofs, lead is still found on some buildings around chimneys, roof valleys, bay windows or even as water pipes. Lead is also used to make the plates in rechargeable lead-acid batteries. Its density is very high at 11.37g/cc.

Lead is a soft, malleable metal with a low melting point of just 327°C. Its strength is only around 15N/mm^2, so it is easily cut or bent to shape without being annealed. Many simple shapes can be formed by hand pressure alone.

It is very corrosion and chemical resistant. Take care when working with lead as its dust and fumes are poisonous. However, working lead is unlikely to cause problems providing hands are washed before touching any food.

Pure lead has little application in the home workshop, although small amounts are useful for adding weight on some models to lower their centre of gravity. The most common use is as ballast weight in locomotives and rolling stock. This can be fitted in the form of lead sheet, cast as lead shot in resin or hot cast to shape. Lead is available in rolls 120mm wide from builder's merchants, or as fishing weights or lead shot from sporting shops.

Lead is usually joined by folding to form a seam or with plumber's solder. Lead will clog up any file and most other tools. Files can be cleaned by rubbing them with a piece of copper.

Figure 3.3 A selection of variously-shaped cast pieces of lead ballast.

Lead is very easily cut to shape with tin snips. Because of its low melting point, lead is extremely easy to melt and cast. Moulds can be made from plaster of Paris, which must be thoroughly dry before the lead is poured.

Lead alloys

Lead is the major component of soft solders and is likely to find widespread use in this form in many models built from metal. Details of its use in solders are given in Chapter 8. Lead is also found in many alloys, such as bearing materials, to improve their lubrication properties.

Lead pigments are used in some paints, though this use is decreasing due to the poisonous nature of such pigments. However, lead is still an excellent metal treatment, for avoiding corrosion, in the form of white lead, red lead and lead chromate paints.

Pewter

Pewter is an alloy of lead and tin that has been used since Roman times for making drinking vessels and plates. It is still used to make tankards and ornamental items. It is available in sheet form and is fairly soft and easy to work. Being harder than

37

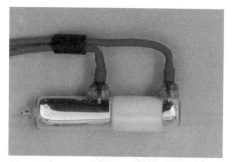

Figure 3.4 A mercury-in-glass electrical tilt switch.

lead, it is more durable. Pewter is grey and takes a good polish. It is usually joined with a special low-melting point soft solder.

Magnesium

As a metal, magnesium is one of the least dense. Its electrical conductivity is only half that of copper and it has a high thermal conductivity. It has little strength and is almost invariably alloyed to improve this characteristic. It melts at 650°C and has a density of only 1.7g/cc. It resists corrosion well except for salt-laden air against which it has little resistance. Its alloys are widely used for making parts for cars and power tools.

Magnesium alloys are very lightweight and their strength-to-weight ratio is better than that of aluminium alloys. They are

also easy to machine and weld. Although unlikely to be needed in the home workshop, some popular alloys are shown in Table 3.1.

Care is needed whenever machining magnesium as dust or fine chips of the material easily ignite and burn fiercely.

Manganese

A constituent of many steel alloys and, of course, of manganese bronze, manganese is otherwise only likely to be found in the average home workshop in the form of electrical resistance wire or, because of its high coefficient of expansion, in electrically-heated expansion elements.

Mercury

As the only common metal which is liquid throughout the temperature range found across the majority of the world, mercury is widely used in barometers and still found in some thermometers, tilt and mercury switches. Its density of 13.6g/cc means that atmospheric temperature will support a practical column of mercury 760mm high. It freezes at -40°C, well below the minimum temperature likely to be experienced in the UK. Always take care when using mercury as both the metal and its compounds are poisonous if ingested.

Alloy	Magnesium	Aluminium	Zinc	Manganese	Zirconium
General purpose wrought	93%	6%	1%	0.3%	
High strength wrought	96.4%		3%		0.6%
General purpose casting (Heat treatable)	91%	8%	0.5%	0.3%	
High strength casting (Heat treatable)	94.8%		4.5%		0.7%

Table 3.1 The constituents of some of the more widely used magnesium alloys.

Molybdenum

Apart from carbon, molybdenum is the most effective element for hardening steel. It is also found in heat-resistant steels where it helps prevent distortion, increases resistance to corrosion and improves creep properties.

Heating elements for electric furnaces, made from molybdenum, can be used up to temperatures of 1650°C. It is also a component of molybdenum disulphide, a useful lubricating material described in Chapter 10.

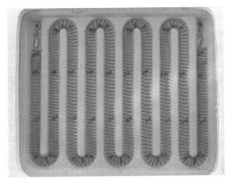

Figure 3.5 Nichrome wire is widely used to make electrical heating elements.

Nickel

Nickel is an excellent engineering material; both tough and ductile. It maintains its strength across a wide temperature range and has good corrosion resistance. It melts at 1455°C and has a strength of about 620N/mm² but its expense makes its use rare in the home workshop. It is straightforward to machine, can be hot- or cold-worked and soldered, brazed and welded. It also exhibits some magnetic properties.

Nickel is widely used in alloys, mainly with excellent corrosion resistance, which maintain their strength at high temperatures. In addition, electrical resistance wire and heating elements are usually made from nickel-chromium alloys of which nichrome wire is probably the most widely known. Nichrome is also excellent for fabricating grates for coal-fired boilers.

Cupro-nickel containing 25% nickel and 75% copper, with traces of manganese, is a popular metal for making 'silver' coins and is used for this purpose in the United Kingdom.

Monel

Monel is a nickel/copper alloy, usually two-thirds nickel and one-third copper, with very small amounts of manganese, silicon, iron, sulphur and carbon.

It resembles nickel silver but is rather less yellow in colour. It melts at over 1200°C. Monel provides relatively high mechanical strength at high temperatures

Alloy	%Ni	Co	%Cu	%Al	%Ti	S	Uses
400	66.5	✓	31.5				Valves, pumps, heat exchangers, marine fittings
405	54.5	✓	44			✓	Valve seat inserts
K500	66.5	✓	29.5	3	0.6		Pump shafts, impellers, scrapers, springs
502	63		27-33	2.5-3.5		✓	Free cutting

Table 3.2 Constituents and uses of different monels. These alloys also frequently contain small amounts of iron, manganese, carbon and silicon.

Name	Condition	Tensile strength	Elongation	Hardness
Monel	Annealed	540N/mm^2	45%	120 Brinell
	Hard	725N/mm^2	20%	220 Brinell

Table 3.3 Typical physical properties of monel in hard and annealed states.

(up to 500°C) or where its high corrosion resistance is required. It is almost as strong as steel, with a tensile strength of 510 - 680N/mm^2 but far more corrosion resistant. It files, drills, hard solders and may be cold-worked quite well. It is a less good conductor than copper.

The alloy first came from Canada where ore deposits contain two-thirds nickel and one-third copper, producing a natural alloy of the two elements when smelted directly from the ore. Monel was the first quality, corrosion-resisting alloy. It therefore finds much use in hospital, laundry and food-handling machinery.

Monel is an extremely tough alloy but is quite expensive and difficult to obtain in small quantities. The cost can be offset against the ability to use thinner sections of monel than steel, due to its resistance to corrosion, and than copper, due to its

Figure 3.5 Nickel silver railway track is excellent at resisting corrosion.

strength. Monel can be welded or brazed and is easily annealed by heating to around 850°C (bright red) and leaving to cool in air.

Monel is useful where strength and corrosion resistance are important. It is an ideal metal for the outer shells of model steam boilers. Its lower conductivity and its strength provide an advantage over copper; its lack of corrosion an advantage over steel. For the model engineer, it is ideal for valves and valve seats and for stays in model boilers. Monel 400 is suitable for use up to more than 500°C while both monel K500 and 502 provide high strength when cold-worked.

Monel is a very tough material that can be machined readily with sharp tools. Monel 405 and 502 have additional sulphur which makes them free cutting.

Sources of supply of monel are not easy to find. Firms making liquid chemical apparatus like dry-cleaning machines may be prepared to sell offcuts. It is sometimes available from surplus suppliers, but is often only obtainable in large quantities from non-ferrous metal stockists.

Nickel silver
Nickel silver, sometimes called German silver, is an alloy of copper, zinc and nickel; normally 20% zinc, 55% copper and 20% nickel. It contains no silver. It gets its name from its silvery appearance. Small quantities of cobalt, lead and iron are often included. The melting point of nickel silver is between 1050°C and 1110°C. It is strong, malleable and corrosion resistant but quite expensive. It has a strength which varies between 200 and

40

Inconel	Ni %	Cr %	Co %	Mo %	Al %	Ti %	Fe %
600	75	15.5					8
601	60.5	23		9	1.4		14.1
625	61	21.5					2.5
690	61.5	29					9
718							
738	61	16	8.5	1.7	3.4	3.4	
X750	73	15			0.8	2.5	6.8

Table 3.4 The constituents of the various inconel alloys.

500N/mm² depending on its constituents and condition. It machines easily and is a good steel substitute for items which will remain unpainted but must not rust. It is not a good electrical conductor but solders well, has relatively good corrosion resistance and takes paint better than brass. In the home it is frequently used in tableware as electroplated nickel-silver (EPNS) and is harder wearing than genuine silverware.

In sheet form it may be obtained as shim and up to 3mm thick, in addition to rounds, flats and extruded sections. It is popular for the construction of small-scale model locomotives and the rails they run on and is also used for making electrical resistance wire.

Nickel silver is readily both soft- and hard-soldered. It is annealed by heating to 600°C – 750°C, a good red heat, and leaving to cool. It can be beaten and pressed to shape, machined, drilled, folded, riveted, sawed and filed with comparative ease. Harder than brass, copper and aluminium, it takes a little more effort when being hand worked, but nothing excessive.

Nickel silver casts well and is used extensively as a steel look-alike in the small-scale model railway field. In the larger scales it is frequently used for live steam locomotive cross heads due to the ease with which castings can be machined and its steel-like appearance.

Inconel

Inconel 600 is a widely used alloy which contains 75% nickel, 15.5% chromium and 8% iron, It has excellent resistance to corrosion and good strength both at normal and high temperatures. It cannot be heat treated but strengthens with cold working. The high chromium content of inconel 601 further improves the metal's corrosion resistance, particularly at high temperatures. 625 is even stronger and the addition of niobium allows it to be welded. Inconel is widely used for making furnace and other heat treatment components as well as hot parts of jet engines. Inconel 713 & 718 are used for cast turbines and nozzle guide vanes for model jet engines.

Figure 3.6 An inconel 718 turbine for a model jet engine.

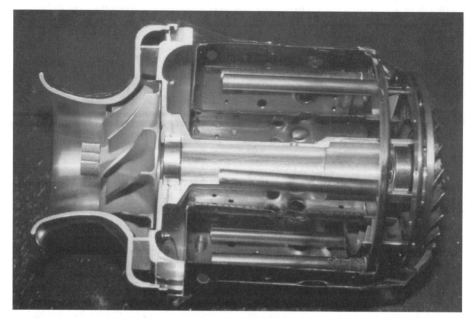

Figure 3.7 The construction of model jet engines requires significant use of inconel or nimonic alloys for the hot, highly stressed components.

Nimonic

The Nimonic alloys are all produced from a base line of 80% nickel and 20% chromium. The addition of some rare-earth elements improves their high temperature characteristics. The nimonic range uses serial numbers which show their ability to operate at increasingly high temperatures. When cold they are sufficiently ductile to be formed into wire, strip, rod, tube and sheet materials. Nimonic alloys are famous for their use in making gas turbine blades, where their superb ability to resist elongation under the highest centrifugal loads, even at elevated temperatures, makes them a natural choice. These qualities make nimonics equally attractive for model gas turbines.

Nimonic	Composition
75	Nickel/chromium with titanium carbide
80A	Nickel/chromium with cobalt, titanium, aluminium and 0.06% carbon
90	Nickel/chromium/cobalt with titanium, aluminium and 0.07% carbon
105	Nickel/chromium/cobalt with molybdenum, titanium, aluminium and 0.2% carbon
115	Nickel/chromium/cobalt with molybdenum, titanium, aluminium and 0.15% carbon

Table 3.5 The constituents of some of the most popular of the nimonic alloys.

Figure 3.8 Some model engineers enjoy working in silver for a change.

Silver

An expensive material, which is very malleable and ductile, silver was originally used for jewellery and coinage. It has the highest electrical and heat conductivity of any metal. However, silver tarnishes badly and has little practical use in the home workshop, apart from its place as a component in silver solder alloys. These are detailed in Chapter 8. As mentioned earlier, nickel silver does not contain any silver, but derives its name from the fact that it looks like silver.

Tin

A soft corrosion-resistant metal, tin lacks strength and has a low melting point of only 232°C. By far its most common use is to coat thin steel sheet to form tinplate. This tin coating, which is completely non-toxic, prevents rusting and is also easy to solder.

Tin is a silver/white shiny metal which is both soft – slightly harder than lead – and malleable. Its strength is only around $30N/mm^2$ and its density is 7.3g/cc. Due to its low melting point, it is also found in many solders and it is a constituent of the alloy pewter.

Figure 3.9 A submarine conning tower made of tinplate salvaged from an old oil can.

Babbitt metal

This is the name for a proprietary white alloy of 89% tin, 7% antimony and 4% copper, used to make bearings. It melts at 239°C and has a Brinell hardness of 35 at room temperature and 15 at 100°C. The name is now applied generically to most white metal bearing alloys using either a tin or lead base.

Tinplate

Tinplate is thin mild steel sheet coated on both sides with a thin layer of tin to prevent rusting. This is the material that was traditionally used for sheet metalwork, though plastics are now taking over in many applications. It is still widely found as containers for tinned foods. It is quite strong for its thickness and resists rusting except along cut edges or where the tin layer has been scratched.

Tinplate is supplied in sheets which are normally 0.38mm, 0.43mm, 0.48mm or 0.54mm thick. It is available in small sheets, typically 700mm x 500mm. It is possible to buy tinplate or salvage it from old food tins or large oil cans. Those with corrugated sides are not much good for recycling. Drinks cans are made either of tinplate or of aluminium and a magnet

Figure 3.10 A parting tool with a tungsten carbide tip brazed onto a mild steel shank, surrounded by larger tungsten carbide tips.

will quickly separate aluminium from tinplate. The material is still useful for making small containers, such as fuel tanks for internal combustion engines.

Tinplate can be soft-soldered, riveted or bolted together. It can also be joined by folding the edges of the joint over each other to form seams.

Tin snips and shears will cut tinplate with ease. It is also easy to bend, fold and curve. When using or storing tinplate avoid scratching the tin coating to prevent rapid rusting. Except where they are going to form an edge, lines should not be marked using a scriber. Mark out instead using a lead pencil or felt tip marker to avoid penetrating the tin layer. Protect finished articles, provided they are clean and grease free, with paint or varnish or 'tin' them with a thin layer of soft solder.

As tin has a relatively low melting point, do not heat tinplate above the temperature necessary for soft soldering. Silver soldering or annealing will ruin it.

Aluminium 'tinplate'
Increasingly popular for fizzy drinks containers, aluminium 'tinplate' is just thin aluminium alloy used to make 'tin' cans.

Titanium

Titanium is a relatively light metal that melts at 1668°C. Its density is a little more than half that of steel at 4.5g/cc. Its alloys are relative modern engineering materials and are attractive because of their:
- High strength-to-weight ratios – 40% lighter than steel but 60% heavier than aluminium.
- Resistance to corrosion.
- Maintenance of their properties up to 550°C.

Titanium alloys are, however, relatively expensive but are widely used in the aerospace industry. The main application in model engineering is for components in model turbojet engines.

Titanium 318
This titanium alloy 6AL4V contains 90% titanium, 6% aluminium and 4% vanadium and accounts for around two-thirds of all titanium alloy materials. It has an excellent strength/weight ratio, excellent corrosion resistance qualities and better thermal conductivity than copper. It can be welded using argon gas.

Tungsten

This is a very dense white metal of great hardness, used in making alloy steels for items such as grinding and other tools, magnets and electrical contacts. It resists oxidation at very high temperatures and is not attacked by most acids. Tungsten wire is used in spark plug electrodes and in light bulbs as the filament.

Tungsten carbide
This material's exceptional hardness makes it the perfect cutting edge for use as lathe tools, mills and masonry drills.

Its high price ensures that the tools only use tungsten carbide tips on mild steel shanks. It is very brittle so that care must be taken to avoid impact loads.

Cemented tungsten carbide is made by incorporating particles of the powdered material in a matrix of metallic cobalt. This improves the toughness of the cutting tool and also provides a degree of self-sharpening by a similar mechanism to that used in grindstone wheels, with fresh particles of tungsten carbide being exposed as blunted ones break away from the cobalt matrix. There are more details about the properties of tungsten carbide in Chapter 7.

Vanadium

Vanadium is an expensive metal found in high strength, low alloy steels where the addition of 0.05% – 0.1% of this metal can double the strength of basic carbon steels. It is corrosion resistant and has a high flexural strength. It is widely used to make chrome-vanadium alloy steels to improve strength, hardness, toughness and fatigue resistance. In tool steels, its wide hardening range makes it popular for quality spanners and its ability to retain its edge makes it a natural material for cutters and dies.

White metal

Commercial white bearing metals, or Babbitt metals, may contain differing amounts of tin or, to reduce cost, lead. Most white metals are lead/antimony/tin alloys, often also including zinc. They are silvery white in colour and have a relatively low melting point. They are widely used for machinery bearings, packings and linings as well as fusible plugs and

Figure 3.11 Zinc castings are popular for the bodies of carburettors.

small decorative castings. Their low melting points make them easy to cast, and those with the lowest melting points can be poured into silicone rubber moulds.

Zinc

Zinc is a metal that is from time to time encountered in sheet form. Like lead, it may be found used for roofing. It may also be the basis of corrosion-resistant containers. It is not as soft as lead, but may still be cold-worked without great difficulty. It has a density of 7.1g/cc. Soft solder and dilute hydrochloric acid flux may be used for joining it.

Zinc melts at 419°C and is a relatively weak blue/white material. However, its main uses are in providing galvanised coatings and in the manufacture of small zinc alloy castings from an alloy often referred to as Mazak which contains magnesium, aluminium and zinc.

Galvanised iron and steel

Zinc is widely found as a coating for iron and steel to prevent rusting and provides a speckled grey finish. The base metal is dipped into molten zinc to form a coating

45

of zinc/iron alloy. Most galvanised material is in sheet form and is useful for making containers that are to remain unpainted as well as in the form of corrugated iron for building workshop sheds. It is also available as galvanised wire, including barbed wire. The addition of a small amount of magnesium significantly improves resistance to corrosion in salt-laden marine environments. Zinc-based primer paints are also excellent for preventing corrosion on welded or brazed joints.

There are many zinc-based alloys and their main use is for die casting because of their low melting points and their corrosion resistance. The end products are light weight and have high accuracy, smooth surface finishes that require little further working. While zinc alloys can be machined, they can only be slightly worked and soldering or welding are not generally possible.

Carbon

Although clearly not a metal, carbon is key in iron and steel making, where controlled amounts result in a wide range of different materials. As graphite, carbon is as an excellent lubricant and graphited metals are used to make self-lubricating bearings and bushes. Graphite is also employed as brushes for electric motors, generators and alternators as well as the lead in pencils. Perversely, in the form of diamond, carbon is also the best abrasive and the hardest substance known. Thin carbon fibres are also used to make an exceptionally strong composite material.

CHAPTER 4

Selecting materials

Choosing the correct material often presents problems to both model and full-size engineers. For those working from plans, a list of the materials needed is usually provided. However, not all the materials quoted may be available and, if the plan is an old one, it may be possible to obtain better materials which may also prove to be cheaper. For those building from scratch, a choice can usefully be made in each of the eight main areas shown in Table 4.1 overleaf.

Shapes and sizes
Metals come in a wide range of forms. Standard materials may be in sheets,

Figure 4.1. Some models, as this one, require a mixture of different metals, wood and plastic.

Mechanical		Physical	Chemical	Environmental
Compression effects.	Self-lubrication.	Density.	Composition.	Low temperature.
Creep resistance.	Shear properties.	Electrical characteristics.	Corrosion resistance.	Room temperature. High temperature.
Ductility.	Stiffness.	Inflammability.	Melting point.	Exposure to:
Elasticity.	Tensile strength.	Thermal expansion.	Adhesive compatibility.	chemicals.
Fatigue resistance.	Wear resistance.	Thermal heat.		salt/sea water. water.
Flexibility.				Environmental
Hardness.				degradation.
Impact strength.				

Dimensional	Availability	Form	Treatment
Dimensional stability.	In workshop.	Bar.	Annealing/tempering.
Flatness.	Local stockist.	Composite.	Case hardening.
Size.	Mail order.	Extrusion.	Casting.
Surface finish.	Minimum order.	Rod.	Drying/seasoning.
Quantity.	Scrap yard.	Sheet.	Painting/varnishing.
	Two-part material.	Special cross-section.	Protective clothing.
		Tube.	Special cutting tools.
			Unit cost.
			Ventilation.

Table 4.1 The main mechanical properties which need consideration in selecting materials.

blocks or strips of varying dimensions. The strips may be formed into square, rectangular, hexagonal, circular, L, U or one of several even more complex shapes. Shim, or shim stock, is thin sheet metal, usually 0.1 – 0.5 mm thick. It is normally supplied in packs containing sheets of varying thickness of brass, copper, nickel-silver, plastic or steel.

Static strength

The ability of any material to resist a steady load for a short period at normal temperatures without breaking or being crushed or deformed defines the strength of the material. The tensile strength is the maximum stretching force which can be applied to the metal without causing it to break.

Item	Elongation %	Tensile strength N/mm^2	1% proof stress N/mm^2	Brinell hardness
Aluminium alloy sheet	18	300	30	80
Wrought copper tube	4	350	90	120
Annealed copper tube	40	210	60	40
Cast iron lathe bed	0.6	215	–	200
70/30 brass cartridges	10	540	460	160
Hot-rolled mild steel plate	25	460	230	130
Alloy steel camshaft	14	1340	1188	400

Table 4.2 Some useful mechanical properties of metals often found in the home workshop.

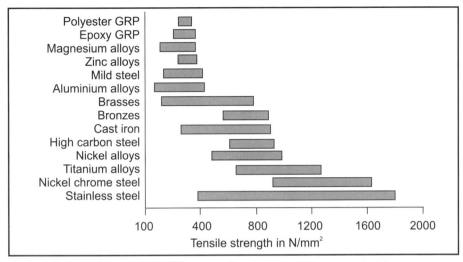

Figure 4.2 A rough comparison of the strengths of some widely used materials.

The 1% proof stress test measures the maximum stretching force which can be applied to a metal causing only a 1% permanent increase in length when the force is removed. Often not of great interest to model builders, some applications, particularly internal combustion engines, make significant demands of the strength of materials. Furthermore, scale-size parts are often more highly stressed than their

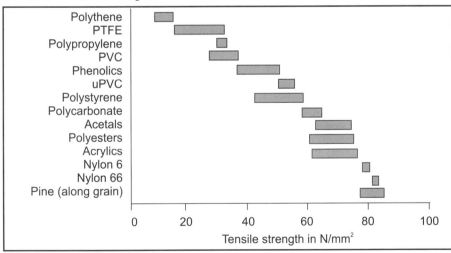

Figure 4.3 The approximate strength of some popular plastic materials compared to pine.

Figure 4.4 Metal offcuts such as these are widely available, usually at minimal cost.

full-size counterparts. Remember, too, that heat treatment and work-hardening both affect the strength of metals.

Sources of supply for metals

Metal stockholders are mostly located in urban areas or on industrial estates. Trade directories and Yellow Pages are good places to start looking. Check under ferrous or non-ferrous metal stockholders.

They are not usually organised to deal with the non-professional user. Many have minimum orders or small quantity handling charges and most charge extra for delivery. They may also only supply uncut material – a 2400 x 1200mm sheet is big and expensive. A bulk order by a model engineering club is a way round this. It is safe to assume that the amount of metal required for most modelling jobs will be considered a small quantity by the majority of stockholders.

Model engineering suppliers and other model shops can supply a wide range of metal shapes and sizes to suit the vast majority of modeller's needs. There are still a few blacksmiths who may sell small amounts of metal to private buyers, but usually only bar or strip steel, or iron.

Many factories which use metal are prepared to sell offcuts. A friend who works for such a company is a useful contact for this purpose. Several firms advertise in magazines such as **Model Engineer** and will supply small quantities of metal by mail. A few of them are listed in Appendix 4.

It is possible to do a lot of metalwork using material otherwise considered as scrap. Sources have been mentioned when considering the individual metals. Do not throw out as junk anything in the home, made of metal, until it has been checked for useful material.

Expanded metal, slit and drawn out into a mesh, is ideal for making grills and vents and can also reinforce plaster work and concrete. Many different types of perforated metal are available, where sheets have actually had holes punched in them.

Wire mesh is a form of metal cloth used to make filters, radiator grilles and the like. It comes in steel and iron, plain, painted or galvanised, copper, brass or monel. Mesh sizes vary from 12 to 400 and are independent of the wire size, apart from the fact that fine meshes must, of necessity, use very fine wires – down to 0.1mm or less – to allow any liquid to pass through the mesh.

Identification of ferrous metals

It is often possible to identify materials simply by their appearance, but Table 4.3 shows a wide range of other tests to assist identification. These include coarse filing, turning in a lathe, or grinding and observing the type of sparks obtained.

Test	Cast iron	Wrought iron	Mild steel
Appearance.	Grey/sandy. Shows line of casting. Bluish sheen.	Red/scaly.	Smooth finish.
Coarse filing.	Very tough skin. Powdery filings.	File drags & clogs Whitish filings. Slag visible.	Less drag than wrought iron. White finish/filings.
Turning in lathe.	Cuts easily. Black crumbly chips/powder when surface wiped.	Poor finish. White curly turnings. Slag lines visible.	Turns easily producing white curly turnings.
Grinding on emery wheel.	Small stream of dull red sparks; sporadic bright burst.	More, lighter sparks than cast iron.	Stream of long white sparks.
Drop bar on hard surface.	Medium metallic sound.	Very dull thud.	Dull, metallic sound.
Saw 1/3rd through 12mm bar, held in vice, 25mm from end. Break off with 1kg hammer.	Snaps easily.	Bends well over.	Bends over, then breaks.
Examine fracture of last test.	Large crystals. Bright specks of free carbon.	Fibrous fracture.	Crystalline fracture.
Hammering at red heat.	Crumbles.	Flattens very easily.	Flattens quite easily.
Quenching from red hot.	No noticeable change. May crack.	No noticeable change.	May slightly harden.

Table 4.3 Test to help identify unknown ferrous metals. More materials are shown in Table 4.4.

However, the sparks from tool steel tend to be very similar whether the metal is in a hard or soft condition. Further tests include dropping the sample and assessing the sound it makes, sawing and breaking, or hammering a hot sample and quenching it.

Unfortunately, many of these tests are destructive in nature so it is worthwhile keeping a small labelled sample of each material which enables a direct physical comparison with the unknown sample and also allows a qualitative assessment of the spark test.

Flame testing

The predominant flame colours seen, when some metals are heated until they are incandescent in a naked flame, are very characteristic and can help with identification:

- Copper   Green/blue
- Lead   Light blue
- Sodium   Yellow
- Zinc   Light green

Magnetic and dip testing

While iron and steel are magnetic, most stainless steel and non-ferrous metals are

51

Test	Medium carbon steel	Carbon tool steel.	High speed steel
Appearance.	Bluish black sheen. Smooth.	Bright black. Very smooth. Sharp corners on square bar.	Rougher than cast steel.
Coarse filing.	As carbon content increases, difficult to make file bite into metal. Surface becomes more glazed as carbon increases.		Not as hard as cast steel.
Turning in lathe.	Increasing hardness under tool. Turnings break into short pieces and may be brown or blue. Rather glazed finish.		Turns fairly easily. Long chips. Distinctive smell from scale.
Grinding on emery wheel.	As carbon content increases, red spark stream becomes more bushy with secondary bursts.		Dull red streaks with forked ends.
Dropping bar on hard surface.	Higher note than mild steel.	High, ringing sound.	Similar ring to mild steel.
Saw 1/3rd through 12mm bar, held in vice, 25mm from end. Break off with 1kg hammer	Bends slightly, then breaks off.	Good resistance to blow.	Good resistance to blow.
Examine fracture of last test.	Fracture finer than mild steel.	Very fine crystalline fracture.	Fine, velvety fracture
Hammering at red heat.	Increasing resistance to flattening as carbon increases.		Considerable resistance to flattening.
Quenching from red hot.	Hard when tested with file.	Hard when tested with file.	Moderately hard.

Table 4.4 Tests to help with the identification of more unknown ferrous metals.

not. The main exceptions are the nickel alloys, which are also often magnetic, and a range of materials used to make magnets.

Stainless and silver steel can be differentiated by dipping a sample in boiler pickle or a copper sulphate solution. While silver steel will become coated with a thin layer of copper, stainless steel will not.

Chemical reactions between metals

One of the major issues when working with different metals that will touch each other, is that a chemical reaction may well take place between them which will cause corrosion to one or both of them. It is useful to understand just what causes this problem. Basically it is similar to the process which occurs in a battery and, of course, most people have seen the serious corrosion problems which are often found around the terminals on old car batteries.

The greater the electrical potential difference between the two metals, the worse the effect. Table 4.6 shows the value of the voltage that is generated

Test	Manganese steel	Stainless steel.	Monel metal
Appearance.	Hard, shiny, bright.	Very shiny, hard.	Bright silver/yellow.
Grinding on emery wheel.	Forked & streaked sparks.	Yellow streaks, pointed at end.	Short faint red streaks.

Table 4.5 A few tests for identifying some more specialist metals. These are nothing like as easy to identify as the metals listed in Tables 4.3 and 4.4.

between some of the more common metals. Thus a copper pipe connected to an aluminium tank generates just over 2 volts. The electrolyte is the moisture in the atmosphere and is, of course, worse if the tank and pipe are filled with water; the worst case of all being the presence of salt water.

The corrosion of metals in contact with water depends on several factors. These include:

- The metal involved – iron rusts, gold is unaffected.
- Metallurgical factors – such as the dezincification of brass.
- Surface defects – allowing water to come into contact with the metal.
- Stress – heavily cold-worked parts corrode more than unworked parts.
- Environmental factors – marine and polluted environments speed corrosion.
- Temperature – chemical reactions speed up as temperature rises.
- Aeration – can increase corrosion by providing additional oxygen.
- Anodic reactions – can form a barrier to corrosion.

Corrosion prevention depends on choosing appropriate materials, careful design and the use of protective coatings. In addition, several environmental factors can have an adverse effect. For example, iron and steel rust in air when water in present; especially rapidly when the water is salty. Some steel alloys, particularly stainless ones, significantly reduce the problems of rusting. However, alloys may suffer stress corrosion.

Aluminium readily develops a durable protective layer. Copper develops a green protective layer when exposed to the atmosphere. This does prevent further corrosion. However, some copper alloys may experience loss of the other major alloying metal rather than corrosion. Zinc develops a hard-wearing oxide layer which resists further corrosion. Protective coatings prevent corrosion, abrasion and wear. They also provide electrical or thermal insulation or conductivity and improve surface appearance.

Ductility
The order of ductility of the more popular metals, with gold the most ductile, is as follows: Gold – Platinum – Silver – Iron – Copper – Aluminium – Nickel – Zinc – Tin – Lead.

Metal	Potential difference in volts
Gold	+ 1.50
Silver	+ 0.86
Copper	+ 0.34
Lead	- 0.13
Tin	- 0.14
Nickel	- 0.25
Iron	- 0.44
Chromium	- 0.74
Zinc	- 0.76
Aluminium	- 1.67
Magnesium	- 2.35

Table 4.6 The voltage generated between some different metals.

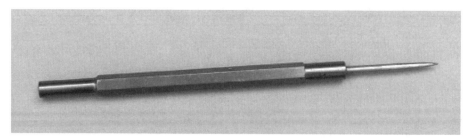

Figure 4.5 The steel point of a scriber must be tempered to the correct degree of hardness.

Hardness

The hardness of a material represents its ability to resist abrasion. For many years, the hardness of minerals has been assessed using Moh's scale, which is shown in Table 4.7. The hardest of all materials is diamond and, at the bottom of the scale, the softest is talc. The hardness of any other substance can be found by establishing which of the standard minerals will just scratch it.

However, Moh does not give sufficient accuracy for substances such as metal alloy. Special tests have been designed and machines built to undertake these tests. It is thus common to find hardness of particular materials quoted in terms of the Vickers, Shore, Rockwell, or Brinell scales. Each uses a slightly different method of measurement, relying on the indentation of a steel ball or pyramid of diamond, drop and rebound of a hammer from a set height or even depth of a scratch.

Hardness Index	Mineral
10	Diamond
9	Corundum
8	Topaz
7	Quartz
6	Orthoclase feldspar
5	Apatite
4	Fluorite
3	Calcite
2	Gypsum
1	Talc

Table 4.7 Moh's scale showing the hardness of certain key materials.

Vickers	Brinell	Rockwell A
100	95	43
200	195	58
300	295	65.2
400	379	70.8
500	471	75.3
600	564	78.6
700	656	81.3
800	722	83.4
900	-	85

Table 4.8 A comparison of Vickers, Brinell and Rockwell A hardness values for steel.

Heat treatment

By heat treating metals, it is possible to harden or soften a great many of them, depending on exactly what is required. Heat treatment is thus an attractive proposition for anyone who has access to a suitable system of heating. To harden steel right through, it is necessary to heat it to a suitable temperature and then quench it in water, brine or oil. Reheating to the right temperature allows the correct degree of temper to be achieved. Many metals work-harden and some just age-harden.

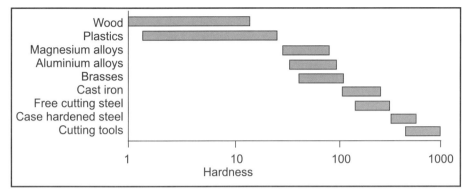

Figure 4.6 The relative hardness of a useful selection of workshop materials.

Most metals can be softened by the process of annealing. This involves heating the metal above a key temperature and then either letting it cool naturally or quenching it in water.

Case hardening

Any substance which can add carbon to the surface of a low carbon steel may be used to add a hardened case to the steel on quenching, while still retaining a soft, ductile centre to it. The case hardening material is usually ordinary charcoal, raw bone or a special carburising compound. These compounds contain charcoal or charred bone usually also with a carbonate of barium, calcium or sodium.

Conductors

Table 4.8 lists the relative conductivity of most commonly-used metals. The comparison is always related to silver; specified as the perfect conductor.

Quite a few models use metal contacts. The primary requirements for this application are good conductivity combined with resistance both to corrosion and wear. Silver is, of course, ideal for this application in conductivity terms but rather expensive as are silver alloys which contain 75% or more silver. However, most requirements only call for small amounts of metal. Nickel brass and nickel silver are low cost alternatives, though with far lower conductivity. Brushes for slip rings or commutators are usually made from carbon which has beneficial lubrication qualities.

Bearing materials

The choice of a bearing material is usually a compromise. The main requirements of

Material	Conductivity compared to silver
Silver	100%
Copper	97.6%
Aluminium	61.5%
Zinc	29.6%
Iron	14.6%
Tin	14.4%
Nickel	12.9%
Steel	11.7%

Table 4.9 The relative conductivity of seven common metals compared with silver.

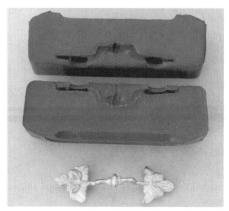

Figure 4.7 A small decorative handle cast in low-melt metal in a silicon rubber mould.

any bearing material, which are seldom all found in a single material are:

- Wear resistance – for long life.
- Low friction coefficient – to reduce the power absorbed and heat generated.
- Tough and ductile – to survive shock loadings.
- Fatigue resistance – to withstand vibrational loads.
- Strength and stiffness – to support loads.
- High thermal conductivity – to get rid of heat generated by friction.
- Corrosion resistance – to avoid deterioration of the bearing surface.
- Permeability – to retain oil, absorb dirt and avoid it causing damage.

White metals and bronzes are often used for bearings though other materials are also suitable. Dissimilar metals are invariably required for shaft and bearing with the wear taken by the bearing.

Some metals and alloys are very well suited for making bearings, because hard crystals occur in a matrix of softer metal, supporting the shaft and allowing free circulation of a lubricant. One metal must have an affinity for lubricants since metal-to-metal contact generates heat and scoring or tearing of the metal.

Wood, one of the oldest of bearing materials, is still excellent for large, low-pressure, slow-speed bearings. Hardwoods absorb oil and grease so little lubrication is necessary and bearings may even made from oil-impregnated wood.

Rubber bearings can be employed if some resilience is essential, lubricated with water. Even plastics are finding an increasing use as materials for bearings, particularly maintenance-free ones based on lubricant-loaded nylons or PTFE.

A few alloy constituents have a catalytic effect on some lubricants. For example, tin in a bearing reduces the tendency of lubricating oil to sludge. An alkali metal can harm an oil, though this is quite rare.

White metal

In general, the tin-based alloys have low coefficients of friction and are tough and capable of withstanding shocks. Babbitt metals are usually limited to 150°C operating temperatures; tin and lead bronzes to 260°C. Small amounts of either nickel or silver increase the strength and hardness of Babbitt metals employed at high temperatures.

Copper alloys

Brass is not good for bearings as its zinc content causes sticking, but the copper bronzes are capable of withstanding reasonably heavy loads. Between the two, almost any desired combination can be obtained, depending upon the proportions of copper, tin, antimony, and lead.

Cast iron

A popular metal for bearings, cast iron is effective because of the significant amount of free carbon, in the form of graphite, which acts as a lubricant.

Aluminium and magnesium alloys

Aluminium bearings have high corrosion resistance, good thermal conductivity, and higher strength than white metal alloys. However, they also have a high coefficient of expansion. Aluminium alloys for bearings usually contain 4% silicon and 4% cadmium. Other alloys include tin, nickel, and copper or silicon. Die-cast magnesium alloy bearings may be found on small items, without inserts or bushings, using a hardened steel shaft.

Plastics

Plastic bearings, with a compressive strength up to 248N/mm², are useful where electrical insulation is needed. For models where lubricating oil is undesirable, plain or impregnated nylon or PTFE bearings are suitable.

Materials like nylon and PTFE are easy to machine to size, are hard wearing and mostly self-lubricating. They thus provide a virtually maintenance-free solution to many bearing requirements. An alternative is the use of ball races made of a plastic, such as Delrin, with steel balls.

Sintered self-lubricating bearings

Self-lubricating bearings may be made of iron or bronze powders, sintered under high pressure and temperature, and impregnated with oil or graphite. Iron is best for low speeds at medium to heavy loads while the bronze is ideal for higher speeds.

Low-melt metals

A few metal alloys melt at remarkably low temperatures. Some even melt in boiling water! These alloys are useful for fittings for some models as the casting can be done in silicone rubber moulds. They are also ideal for making boiler plugs and the ones which melt below 100°C are perfect

Material	Coefficient of expansion
Cast iron	0.000010
Steel	0.000011
Nickel	0.000014
Copper	0.000017
Brass	0.000019
Silver	0.000019
Aluminium	0.000024
Zinc	0.000027
Tin	0.000028
Magnesium	0.000029

Table 4.10 The unit length increase per °C change in temperature of some key metals.

for filling tubes prior to bending. Wood's alloy typically contains 50% bismuth, 25% lead, 12½% tin and 12½% cadmium. It melts at just over 70°C. Boiler plug alloys will need a higher melting point and a number of proprietary metals can be purchased with a range of melting temperatures above 100°C.

Low expansion alloys

Alloys exist in a large variety, mainly made from nickel and iron, that have very low coefficients of expansion. They are widely used when making clock pendulums or scientific instruments. The most widely known alloy is Invar; a relatively soft metal which has the lowest expansion coefficient of all metals at temperatures up to 177°C. In the range from -10°C to +25°C its rate of expansion is only 1.44 millionths per °C. Heat treatment and cold working can reduce this low figure to zero or even a negative value at room temperatures.

Magnetic materials

Steels are rarely used today as magnets, many more effective alloys having been

Figure 4.8 A sintered magnet salvaged from the motor of an old video recorder.

developed. Magnetic materials divide into non-permanent and permanent types. The former are used for electromagnets and include iron, and alloys of iron with silicon or nickel. For the latter, cobalt is the main constituent.

The Alnico range of magnetic alloys is based on a majority of iron, with small amounts of aluminium, cobalt, copper, nickel and sometimes titanium, to provide particularly good magnetic qualities.

Ferrite or soft ceramic magnets have a base of iron oxide together with magnesium, nickel or zinc oxides. This composition results in magnets which are highly resistant to demagnetisation. Rare-earth magnets are as much as ten times stronger than other magnets. They are formed by binding powders made from materials such as samarium-cobalt or caesium-cobalt.

Standards

There are three main standards used to define metals in the UK:
- BS or British Standards.
- BS EN or European Standards – not to be muddled with the old EN numbers.
- ISO or International Standards.

In the United States, life is not so easy. Rather than AS numbers as American standards might be called, there is the following range of numbering systems.:
- ASTM – American Society for Testing and Materials.
- Iron and steel – AISI or American Iron & Steel Institute standards.
- Copper – CDA or Copper Development Association standards.
- Aluminium – A four digit numerical designation also used in the UK.

"The specifications given in our catalogues", one well-known supplier stated, "are what our own supplier quotes to us!"

The thickness of wire and sheet metal is measured in millimetres. Occasionally the abbreviation mm is omitted, so that 0.1mm sheet is referred to as 0.1 thick.

CHAPTER 5

Plastics

Plastics are much more widely used in the average home workshop than might be expected. Most machine tools feature plastic drive belts, while file handles, soft-headed hammers and soft vice jaws may also be plastic. Other items range from Loctite adhesives to O-rings and seals. PTFE bearings, delrin gears and epoxy putties are becoming increasingly popular while GRP is often used to construct diesel and electric locomotive bodies.

It is not that easy to specify which plastics model engineers are likely to use.

It is, however, relatively straightforward to define engineering plastics; materials like acetal and nylon.

Many model engineers like to use other plastics such as composite materials, clear plastic sheeting, specialist plastic-based adhesives, foams, silicone rubber and synthetic rubber belts, seals and tyres.

Hot air engines often have displacers made from expanded polystyrene, while their cylinders and other parts from may use transparent acrylic. Thus this chapter

Figure 5.1 Plastic tools and gauges are becoming increasingly useful in the home workshop.

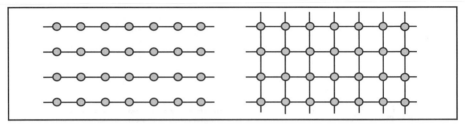

Figure 5.2 A typical thermoplastic molecule, left and thermoset molecule right.

will examine a wider range of plastics than might initially be expected, although polythene, useful in clear sheet and as storage bags, will get no further mention.

A few plastics occur in nature, such as rubber and shellac, but almost all those used in model engineering are man-made. The earliest of these date from the mid-nineteenth century though the majority have been produced by the petroleum industry since the 1930s.

Most plastics and synthetic rubbers are excellent electrical insulators. This superb insulation quality often causes a build-up of static electricity, though additives have reduced this problem. However, it can be

Figure 5.3 A Wimshurst machine clearly showing its plastic insulating discs.

a nuisance when preparing plastics for painting or cleaning transparent materials.

Plastics consist of long-chain molecules called polymers. In thermoplastics they are able to slide past each other.

In thermosetting plastics, links between the chains mean they cannot be reshaped by reheating after they have been initially formed. A few plastics do not actually fall into either category.

Thermoplastics can be softened and reshaped by the application of gentle heat. This means taking care, when they are used in heat engines, to avoid distorting or melting them. Thermosetting materials are rigid and once formed cannot be reshaped. Some plastics are mixed together during manufacture to enhance particular properties. Styrene-butadiene rubber is an alloy of butadiene and styrene.

Plastics are good insulators, making it hard to heat a sheet of thermoplastic to an even temperature throughout. Their large heat capacity means they retain their heat well once hot. Plastics are four to eight times worse than wood as insulators but thousands of times better than a metal like copper. Plastics also expand and contract when heated or cooled; some up to eight times as much as the average metal. All plastics tend to become more brittle as their temperature falls.

Most polymers embody some additive to improve their qualities. These include fillers for better impact and heat resistance, pigments for colouring and plasticisers for softening. Thermosetting plastics often use catalysts to speed up their chemical setting reaction. Other additives provide anti-static properties, flame and smoke retardation, foaming, lubrication, mould release and reinforcement. Stabilisers and anti-oxidants help plastics survive in the environment and solvents assist cleaning and welding thermoplastics together.

Engineering thermoplastics

Thermoplastics can stretch and then revert to their original size when the force is released, providing their elastic limit is not exceeded. None, however, stretches as much as rubber. The main engineering thermoplastics are acetal, polyamides (nylons) and PTFE.

Acetal (polyacetal)
Among the strongest and stiffest of all the thermoplastics, acetal is a fairly dense, fine-looking white plastic. It combines first-class mechanical properties with good chemical resistance, though it is attacked by some acids. Its moisture absorption and coefficient of friction are relatively low while its abrasion resistance and dimensional stability are excellent. It can withstand water up to 115 °C and is slow to burn. These properties are similar to nylon but acetal absorbs much less water and has better abrasion resistance.

Acetal is good for engineering applications where these characteristics are needed. Its dimensional stability is useful when making close tolerance parts. Acetal is available in sheet or rod form suitable for machining. Typical uses include blower wheels, fan blades, gears, pump impellers and sprockets and it is also found in plumbing fittings.

Figure 5.4 Flexible suds pipes are usually made from acetal.

Delrin is Du Pont's proprietary form of acetal, which is easier to machine and has better mechanical properties, apart from its resistance to hot water and alkaline liquids. Its tensile strength is 68N/mm². Black delrin is suitable for exposure to sunlight, assuming that the colour is not a problem. Delrin worms and wheels are

Figure 5.5 Delrin is used to make gears which are economic in cost and run quietly.

61

Figure 5.6 It is not a good idea to use nylon for a bearing to be immersed in water.

a satisfactory alternative to phosphor bronze running against steel or against each other. Delrin spur or helical gears have about the same power rating as similarly-sized brass gears. Duracon is another proprietary acetal, mainly used for making injection-moulded gears.

PEEK (polyether ether ketone)

Victrex, a commercial form of PEEK, is closely related to acetal. It is a high-performance engineering plastic which is strong and rigid. It has excellent high temperature characteristics (up to 250°C) and has a tensile strength of 92N/mm^2. It withstands steam and high pressure water applications and is highly resistant to most liquids.

Figure 5.7 A length of torlon ready to be drilled and tapped.

Polyamides

The group of long-chain thermoplastics, known as polyamides, are extremely strong in the direction of their filaments, as is typified by the strength of nylon thread.

Nylon

Nylon comes in several distinct forms. The rigid type is an important engineering material that can be used in load-bearing applications. It has a low coefficient of friction and machines well, but tends to absorb moisture. It is tough, rigid, relatively heat resistant and less affected by oils, greases and abrasion than most non-ferrous metals! It is useful for making items such as bearings, bushes, cams, gears, nuts, bolts and washers, rollers, and valve seats.

Nylon 66 is probably the most widely used engineering plastic. It is white with a high melting point (260°C), excellent mechanical properties, good electrical characteristics and resistance to chemicals. It is ideal for making parts which must wear only very slowly and require little lubrication.

Glass-filled nylon 66, a dark grey 30% glass – 70% nylon mix, has increased strength and stiffness, with a tensile strength of 190N/mm^2. It withstands continuous temperatures up to 110°C and 200°C for short periods.

Cast nylon 6 is a natural-coloured material which is free of internal stresses, making it ideal for machining. It is not affected by most chemicals, including salt water, and has a high abrasion resistance.

MoS$_2$ filled, cast nylon 6 is black, due to its molybdenum disulphide content. The result is a low-friction material which is self-lubricating. It is tough and abrasion resistant with a melting point of 230°C.

Nylatron GS incorporates molybdenum disulphide in a nylon 66 base. It is more expensive than MoS_2 filled, cast nylon 6 but has similar properties. It is used to make bushes, gears and rollers.

Nyloil is a creamy-yellow coloured oil-filled nylon. It has the lowest coefficient of friction of any nylon. It also has a high resistance to water absorption. A free-cutting material, it is easily machined to tight tolerances and smooth finishes.

Torlon
A plastic with some excellent physical properties and chemical resistance, torlon is strong in compression and has a fine resistance to impact. Its tensile strength is 163N/mm². It will operate for long periods at up to 230°C, but is severely affected by steam at as low as160°C. It also has a low coefficient of expansion.

Bearing-grade torlon is green/black with added fluorocarbon and graphite to reduce friction. It is wear resistant with a high compressive strength. It can operate at quite high temperatures making it ideal for applications such as bearings, piston rings, thrust washers and wear pads. Electrical grade torlon is an excellent, dark brown coloured, electrical insulator, widely used in components like relays and switches.

Tufnol
The excellent mechanical and electrical properties of tufnol are combined with low water absorption. Brown coloured, it comes in several different forms with varying characteristics. Carp-brand tufnol is a laminate based on a fine weave, quality fabric. It is used to make small-toothed gears and other precision components such as thrust washers, insulators, and rollers. Kite brand is a readily machinable form of tufnol which is supplied in rod and sheet form.

Tufnol is widely used to make electrical items, due to its excellent high-voltage

Figure 5.8 Leaf springs are often made from tufnol rather than steel to give a more realistic deflection under load.

insulation properties. It may also be drilled and tapped. Whale brand is a medium weave, quality fabric-laminated plastic supplied both in sheet and rod form.

10G/40 comes in rod form and is an epoxy glass laminate of tufnol which has excellent electrical and mechanical characteristics. It is good insulator regardless of humidity and is also both rigid and dimensionally stable. Tufnol helical and spur gears can transmit about the same power as similar brass ones.

Tufnol leaf springs
Laminated tufnol strip is useful for making scale leaf springs both for road and railway vehicles and is sold in a range of sizes for this purpose from 9mm x 0.8mm to 19mm x 1.5mm in 1220mm lengths. It deflects under lighter loads than the steel equivalent, making scale deflections possible, and it never rusts.

PTFE (polytetrafluoroethylene)
Also called teflon or fluon, PTFE is a dense plastic and one of the most costly. Its main attraction in model engineering results from its remarkably low friction coefficient (0.02 - 0.1), making it the

Figure 5.9 An acrylic displacer cylinder, with an expanded polystyrene displacer.

perfect material for making lightly-stressed bearings, as a surface coating and as a powdered additive to lubricants. It resists almost every chemical better

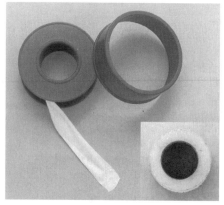

Figure 5.10 PTFE tape for sealing joints and, inset, a very low friction PTFE bearing.

than all other plastics. It withstands quite high temperatures (250°C) as well as very low ones and is a superb insulator.

PTFE is readily machined, though it starts decomposing at 270°C, producing poisonous fumes. Never ever smoke when machining this plastic as dust could be drawn through cigarette/cigar/pipe during the machining process.

PTFE is used to make bearings, gaskets, packings, seals, valves and pump parts, and as a lubricant additive. PTFE tape is used to make waterproof screwed joints. Wrapped round the male portion before insertion into the female part, it is a first-class jointing material. With an exceptional low coefficient of friction, a teflon spray is ideal for treating slide ways and shafts.

Viton

A proprietary Du Pont material, viton is a vinyl-based plastic with a high tensile strength (130N/mm^2). It can withstand continuous temperatures of 200°C and intermittent exposure to 315°C. It is very resistant to hydrocarbons, solvents, steam and water. It is widely used to make O-rings, popular for steam engine glands, but can also liberate dangerous fumes if seriously overheated.

Other useful thermoplastics

Although not strictly engineering plastics, there are several other thermoplastics which are often used by model engineers.

Acrylic (polymethyl methacrylate)

A hard, rigid, but rather brittle material, acrylic has a superb surface finish which weathers and machines well. It has a high rate of thermal expansion and should not be used above 100°C. It also absorbs a small amount of water when immersed. Its uses include light covers, safety glass and spectacles as well as any parts which need to be transparent.

Perspex (polymethyl acrylate)
A common form of acrylic is perspex. It is manufactured in clear and opaque forms in many different colours. In its clear form, it outperforms most glass and is shatterproof. It can be extruded to form pipes which will transmit a high proportion of light along their length regardless of bends; useful for providing lights in some models.

Cellulose plastics (celluloid)
Cellulose is found in plant life including wood. It is not widely used today because of its inflammability and poor chemical properties. All cellulose-based plastics are very tough and well able to resist impacts. They also have an excellent appearance and are available as transparent sheets which are easy to vacuum form.

CAB (cellulose acetate butyrate), often called just butyrate, is a current variant of cellulose with low water absorption and weather resistance. It is easy to mould and the resulting shapes have excellent optical properties. It is pliable, machinable and very durable. It is ideal for representing the glass or perspex in any model and is a good choice for windscreens and other glazing.

Polycarbonate
Widely available as a virtually unbreakable, optical-quality, sheet material, polycarbonate has good mechanical properties including superb impact resistance.

It is harder to mould than the other thermoplastics and twice as expensive. It is fire resistant and only absorbs little moisture. It survives temperatures up to 135°C and is used for making battery covers, CDs and safety goggles.

Figure 5.11 A model crane will typically use polyester cord to lift the load.

Polyester
Thermoplastic polyester is the basis of terylene (or dacron) thread and fabric. Polyester is also used to make blow-moulded bottles for aerated drinks. Copolyesters are variants of polyester made by reaction with other materials. A common form is clear copolyester

Figure 5.12 CAB and polycarbonate are popular as a glazing material for models.

Figure 5.13 A blow-moulded bottle can be used as a low-pressure air storage vessel.

Figure 5.14 A plastic knob made from PVC.

sheet, which can withstand temperatures up to 250°C and is pliable and stress resistant. Fizzy drinks bottles have some application as low-pressure compressed air reservoirs in a wide range of models.

Polypropylene
Quite a hard and glossy plastic, polypropylene floats in water. It can withstand the effects of boiling water for a short time. Its impact strength is not that high and it becomes quite brittle around freezing temperatures.

It is widely used for injection-moulded items. A particularly useful characteristic is its resistance to fatigue and stress cracking when flexed, making it a good hinging material. It is commonly used both for making pin-less hinges and for containers with integrally hinged lids.

Expanded polystyrene (styrene)
A lightweight but brittle material with an exceptionally low thermal conductivity, expanded polystyrene is best cut to shape with a hot wire, though a sharp serrated knife or razor saw will suffice. It is available in a white form and as a denser but significantly stronger blue type. Foam densities differ but, typically, white foam is 20gm/1000cc. Expanded polystyrene is widely used as packaging for new electronic equipment and is a popular material for Stirling engine displacers.

PVC or vinyl (polyvinyl chloride)
One of the most widely manufactured plastics, PVC is quite a hard and relatively uninflammable. Three variants are common, UPVC (unplasticised), PPVC (plasticised) and increasingly CPVC (chlorinated), the latter due to its resistance to distortion and combustion at higher temperatures.

The quantity of plasticiser added to the raw PVC varies from a little in unplasticised to a high proportion in the flexible types. PVC is scratch and corrosion resistant. It is used to make water piping, a range of containers and electrical fittings. DIY stores hold stocks of PVC in the form of sheet material, guttering, soil and water pipes.

Plasticised PVC is used to make hose pipes and leather cloth and is found covering the wires of electric flex. Fablon and similar products are PVC self-adhesive plastic film materials in many colours and patterns including baize and simulated wood.

Grey PVC is a rigid material which is easy to machine and straightforward to weld using solvent. It is useful for making handles and knobs.

Thermosetting plastics

Thermosetting plastics set by chemical reaction during forming or moulding. They are both rigid and hard. Once formed, they can be cut but not reshaped. They are popular because the chemical reaction can take place in the workshop. Thermosetting plastics form the basis of GRP and other composite materials.

Epoxy
Widely known as the adhesive Araldite, epoxy two-part adhesives are excellent for joining metals and many other types of material. More details are given in Chapter 8. Epoxy resin is widely used for making quality GRP mouldings as well as carbon and kevlar-based composites. Epoxy resin is also used as a finish on timber and is an economic way of providing a smooth coating on patterns and forms. Epoxy putties and composites are described later in this chapter.

Phenolics and formaldehyde coatings
The original hard thermosetting plastics, phenolics are tough substances which

Figure 5.15 Many thermoplastics are extruded to form a variety of strips of different cross-section.

resist heat and most chemicals. They are glossy and inexpensive, stable up to 200°C, with a few able to withstand short-term exposure up to 300°C. Their electrical insulation properties are only acceptable at low humidities.

Phenol formaldehyde is a dark-coloured material and a common trade name is Bakelite. It is a low-cost, rigid material still used by the electrical industry.

Phenolic laminates are strong, rigid, machinable and come in sheet, tube and moulded form. Because of their colour, they are often given a coat of melamine, Paxolin is a proprietary name for a paper-reinforced phenolic laminate which is an excellent insulator and, despite its brown colour, is used to make a wide range of electrical components and low-grade printed circuit boards.

Melamine formaldehyde (MF) and urea formaldehyde (UF) are hard, tough, scratch- and stain-resistant materials. They also have good abrasion resistance and are self-extinguishing. Glass- and metal-filled variants are quite dense. Their

Figure 5.16 Silicone rubber is used here to provide flexible couplings on a hot air engine.

expense means they are usually found only as very thin coatings on phenolic laminates.

Formica and similar products are phenolic laminates coated with melamine. When glued to chip board, they form a perfect work surface for machine tools as they are easy to clean and relatively heat-proof.

Polyester
Polyester resin is widely used for making glass reinforced plastic. It is smelly but less expensive than epoxy resin. Polyester resins are slightly coloured and, when mixed with a catalyst, set quite quickly. Isopon is an easily-sanded polyester filler used to repair dents and scratches in car bodies. It also useful for undertaking similar repairs in metal and GRP models.

Polyurethane
By varying the proportions of the two constituent parts forming these plastics, the characteristics can be varied to provide adhesives, foams, moulded sheets, rubbers and surface coatings.

Polyurethane foam, though heavier than expanded polystyrene, has even better insulation properties and is flexible. It comes in aerosol cans which produce an amazing quantity of foam from their relatively small size. The foam adheres to most other materials.

Polyurethane rubbers have excellent tensile strength. They resist tearing and abrasion but are relatively hard and unresilient. Polyurethane is used to make forklift truck tyres, rubber oil seals and varnishes.

Tufset
A rigid pale-blue polyurethane plastic, tufset is dimensionally stable and very abrasion resistant. It is unaffected by most chemicals but direct sunlight causes slow yellowing. Tufset suffers little from stress cracking or fatigue. It is easily machined to a close tolerance, quality finish. Tufset is excellent for making items such as bearings, bushes, gears and wear strips.

Silicone
Room-temperature vulcanising silicone rubbers are heat-resistant, low shrinkage and unaffected by other materials. These factors, together with their elasticity, make them ideal for gaskets, seals, and sealants. Silicon rubber is also useful for making items such as rubber tyres for small-scale model traction engines and other vehicles. The ingredients are not too expensive but have only a short shelf life. Most silicone rubbers are two-part materials. However, silicone bath sealant is a one-part substance.

Figure 5.17 Synthetic rubber is perfect for making small traction engine and lorry tyres.

Figure 5.18 A silicone rubber seal being cast in place on a model submarine's deck.

The following two-part silicone rubbers are from the Alec Tiranti range.

- RTV-11 – a free-flowing, white, general-purpose rubber able to withstand exposure continuously to 200°C; occasionally to 260°C.
- RTV-31 – the firmest, red-coloured rubber. Survives 260°C continuously; 315°C occasionally.
- RTV-420 – a strong, soft white-coloured, condensation-cure rubber that is flexible and tear resistant.
- RTV-428 – similar to but firmer than RTV-420.

Three different catalysts, when mixed with these silicone rubbers, allow them to cure. The choice depends on the grade of rubber and desired cure time. Additives make the silicone rubber thicker, stronger, thixotropic (non-drip) or coloured. There is also a silicone rubber release agent for treatment of mould boxes, normally supplied as an aerosol spray, and a silicone fluid for thinning silicone rubber and cleaning bushes.

Silicone rubber is also used to make white 'steam quality' O-rings which are ideal for glands and packing.

Silicone tube is popular both for oil and fuel pipes on model steam engines and internal combustion engines that run on alcohol-based fuels.

Silicone fluids are anti-stick and water-repellent. They have low surface tension making their popularity widespread. Direct uses of spray-on silicone include lubrication of machine tool parts and protection of electrical contacts from water. Other typical applications include additives to barrier creams, lubricants and greases, paints and polishes, release agents and water-repellent coatings.

Synthetic rubber (diene and olefin rubbers)

Synthetic rubbers, often just referred to as rubbers, are elastomers which differ from other plastics only in terms of their ability to stretch (defined as doubling their length) and return immediately to their original shape. For modelling requirements, the main use of these materials is for diaphragms, O-rings, seals, tyres for vehicles, anti-vibration mounts and shock mountings.

BR (butadiene rubber)

BR is one of the least expensive synthetic rubbers. It has excellent resistance to

69

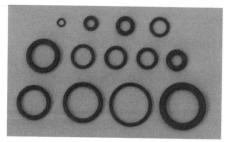

Figure 5.19 O-rings, made from synthetic rubber have solved many model engineering sealing problems.

abrasion, flexing and tearing and has a very low gas and air permeability; useful for diaphragms, hoses, inner tubes and other tubing.

CR (Chloroprene rubber) and neoprene

Chloroprene rubber is the main synthetic rubber not used for making vehicle tyres. It resists oils and heat better than SBR or NBR. It is used for making adhesives, car parts and covering wire.

Du Pont neoprene is an airtight CR which is also relatively unaffected by petroleum products. It is also quite heat resistant, maintaining its properties up to 120°C. These characteristics make it popular for use in internal combustion engines. In both sheet and tube form, it is widely used for making diaphragms, engine mounts and gaskets.

Isoprene

True synthetic natural rubber, isoprene has very similar characteristics to the natural product. It is slightly more elastic and is easily injection moulded. It is relatively oil resistant and used to make gaskets, O-rings and seals.

Natural rubber

A resin extruded from several plants and trees, natural rubber has been replaced in most applications by one of the many synthetic equivalents which better resist fuels and oils. It is still used to make erasers and is also found as latex that is used in contact adhesives and dipped products such as balloons and gloves.

NBR (nitrile rubber)

NBR is a low-cost, hard-wearing synthetic rubber. It has better low-temperature properties than natural rubber but eventually becomes hard and brittle. It is also outstanding in its resistance to oil and fuels. It is often used to make O-rings.

NBR, the basis of Klingersil, is a synthetic, composite, jointing material. It is costly but is perfect for use with air, steam, oils and fuels. Depending on the grade, it will stand steam up to 290°C, temperatures of 450°C and pressures up to 130 bar. Three grades of compressed synthetic-fibre sheet are:

- A jointing material with anti-stick surfaces, made of glass fibre with an NBR binder.
- A green gasket material of aramid fibres with an NBR binder, for use in internal combustion engines and compressors.
- A black jointing material made of carbon fibre in an NBR binder. It is a direct replacement for asbestos and is perfectly suited to hot, high-pressure steam applications.

SBR (styrene-butadiene rubber)

With similar properties to NBR, SBR is a synthetic rubber that is readily produced to a uniform consistency. While cheap and hard-wearing, its main shortcoming is its lack of resistance to oil. It is better at low-temperatures than natural rubber but age hardens and becomes brittle. Like natural rubber, it can be vulcanised and is the most widely used synthetic rubber, mainly for making vehicle tyres. These

Material	Pressure	Max temperature	Rotation speed
Pure PTFE	200 bar	280°C	7 m/s
PTFE/graphited GFO fibre	200 bar	280°C	10 m/s
Kevlar/aramid fibre	400 bar	280°C	15 m/s

Table 5.1 The fine performance characteristics of some plastic-based gland packing materials.

may be fitted to a range of working models and trailers from traction engines to cars for children to sit in and drive. It has no other application in model engineering.

Flexible pipes

Flexible pipes are produced in a great many different plastic materials and are useful for air compressor connections, gas, lubrication and steam pipes. Silicone rubber tube resists heat well, but is fairly soft and vulnerable in harsh environments. It is attacked by petrol and diesel fuels. Neoprene and most clear plastic tube are impervious to attack by these liquids. Reinforced plastic piping is ideal for compressed air leads. Plug-together systems for pumping suds use acetal components to build up pipe work.

Gaskets and seals

Gaskets and seals are important to the construction of internal combustion and steam engines and their gearboxes. Loctite 542 is a steam-proof gasket for cylinders and steam chests. Nitrile rubber or viton O- or V-rings and nitrile-rubber cord, joined with cyano glue, are useful at the ends of gauge glasses on boilers.

Gland packings made from pure PTFE, PTFE/graphited GFO fibre or kevlar/aramid fibre all withstand high pressures, reasonable temperatures and rotation speeds. PTFE tape is ideal for sealing low-pressure water pipes.

Fillers and putties

A range of fillers and putties is available, some made from natural ingredients; the majority from thermosetting plastics. The latter are useful for filling small imperfections in metal castings and wooden forms, making small components for scales models and changing the shape of existing components.

Chemical metal and wood

There are many proprietary fillers, usually polyester thermosetting plastics supplied in two parts; the paste and the hardener. Typically hardening in ten minutes once they have been mixed, different variants can be used to fill metal, GRP and wood work as well as concrete and stone.

Some are reinforced and others have been specially formulated for repairing leaks in fuel and water tanks. Widely available from accessory and DIY stores, two popular brand names are Plastic Padding and Isopon.

Putty

A mixture of calcium carbonate and linseed oil, putty is mainly used as a caulking material for securing glass in window frames but is sometimes also used as a filler for patterns.

Epoxy putty

Two-part epoxy putties such as Milliput and Ferro-plast have a soft putty-like consistency when mixed but cure chemically and set so hard they can be drilled, tapped and machined. They adhere to metal,

Typical Properties	A1	S1	S2	S3	Strip	Syringe
Consistency	Putty	Putty	Liquid	Putty	Putty	Liquid
Pot life minutes at 20°C	60	60	60	8	10*	4
					* Apply within 5 mins	
Initial cure at 20°C	12hr	12hr	12hr	30min	30min	30min
	After seven days cure at 23°C					
Hardness (Shore D)	85	85	85	85	75	85
% shrinkage	0.1	0.1	0.1	0.5	–	–
Tensile shear strength						
on steel: N/mm²	20	20	25	20	7	17
on aluminium: N/mm²	15	20	20	12	5	15
Compressive strength						
(1cm thick film) N/mm²	70	70	70	60	40	80
Tensile strength: N/mm²	50	60	65	45	13	15
Min temperature °C	-20	-20	-20	-20	-20	-20
Max temperature °C	+120	+120	+120	+120	+120	+120
Occasional exposure °C	+150	+150		+150	+150	+150

Table 5.2 The properties of the Loctite range of Metal Set resins and putties.

wood and most plastics. They are popular for providing reinforcement and as fillers.

Epoxies exhibit virtually no shrinkage and can be formed into complete small components for attachment to models. An alternative is the use of epoxy glue in a plasticine mould.

Milliput is typical of commercially available epoxy putties. It comes in two-parts (yellow/grey). The constituents have a reasonable shelf life but once mixed the putty is soft and highly adhesive. It then gradually hardens. Speed of curing to rock hard at room temperature is two to three hours.

The application of heat can reduce this to a few minutes. After setting the putty becomes fully cured after a period equal to the setting time, at the same temperature. Once fully cured it can be drilled, filed, machined, sawed, sanded and tapped. It is heat resistant up to 130°C.

Milliput will bond to concrete, glass, metal, plastic and wood. It will fill dents and scores in casting and sheet metal work, repair leaking tanks and make knobs and small parts for models. It is typical of modern epoxy putties.

Loctite Metal Set products

These two-part filled epoxy resins are grey in colour and are ideal for the repair and recovery of worn and damaged metal work. Typical applications include repairing broken or damaged components like castings, fabrications and pipes as well as mending flanges, housings, key ways and shafts. The Loctite range comprises:

A1 – A fine textured, low weight aluminium-filled epoxy putty.

S1 – A steel-filled epoxy putty for general repairs.

S2 – A liquid variant of S1 for easy pouring and moulding.

S3 – A fast-curing steel-filled epoxy putty for rapid repairs.

Metal Set Strip - A tape with an outer layer of fast-curing epoxy putty and an inner core of hardener which are mixed by hand-kneading.

Metal Set Syringe – A mineral-filled epoxy contained in a small hand-held

Type of material	Relative tensile strength	Relative compressive strength	Relative strength-to-weight ratio
GRP chopped strand mat	1	1	1
GRP plain weave fabric	2.7	1.7	1.6
GRP rovings	6	2.4	2
Kevlar composite	4.7		2.8
Carbon fibre composite	3.4		4.2

Table 5.3 The relative strength of various composite materials.

twin syringe for accurate dispensing of small quantities.

Once functional strength has been achieved, the material can be worked with normal hand tools but full strength continues to develop for some time after this. Surfaces to be bonded or filled should be clean and free of grease, rust or other loose particles.

If Metal Set is used for moulding, a release agent (wax, grease or silicone) will prevent it adhering to the mould. Store these products in dry conditions from 15 to 30°C and keep containers tightly closed when not in use.

Shims

Plastic shim, colour coded in thickness from 0.05mm to 0.5mm is suitable for most of the same jobs as metal shim. The thinner sheets are usually made from polyester; the thicker ones from polypropylene. A particular benefit is that because of their insulation properties, they can be used to prevent electrical current flow between parts of a model and corrosion between dissimilar metals.

Storage of plastics

Plastics such as polyester resin, silicone rubber, anaerobic and cyano glues only have shelf lives of a few months. This can often be extended by refrigeration. Manufacturers usually recommend the best way to store these materials.

Store plastic sheet and rod vertically or flat to avoid warping. Scraps can go in a suitable box, but avoid mixing soft, damage-prone plastics, like expanded polystyrene, with harder materials.

Composite materials

A number of properties make the use of composites increasingly popular for the fabrication of anything from a complete diesel locomotive body to a small component. These include:

- High impact strength and resilience combined with low weight.
- Dimensional stability and ease of colouring.
- Waterproof and resistant to fuels and oils.
- Low thermal expansion, particularly with carbon or kevlar fibres.

By far the most widely used composite material is GRP or glass reinforced plastic, also called fibre glass. Becoming much more popular for highly-stressed parts, but significantly more expensive, are both carbon and kevlar reinforced plastics.

The reinforcement for composites is in the form of thin threads, mats or woven fabrics.

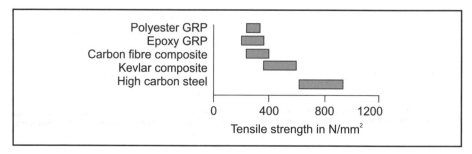

Figure 5.20 The tensile strength range of some composite materials compared with steel.

The resin used may be one of three:
1. Polyester, which is low cost, easy to work but with a strong odour.
2. Epoxy resin, which is more expensive and not as easy to work.
3. Relatively new acrylic resins which exhibit low shrinkage rates.

Most epoxy resin-based materials have excellent resistance to industrial liquids and solvents such as water, caustic soda and hydrocarbons.

Flat GRP laminate, in the form of electronic printed circuit board, can also find uses for making small components. It can either have the copper coating left in place, or it can be removed by dissolving it in an etching solution.

The strength of composites

There are several factors which influence the strength of finished composites. The first, and most obvious, is the type of reinforcing material selected but the form of the material, number of layers, type of resin and proportion of resin are also significant. Regardless, the ultimate strength of the composite will take a few days to develop once the work has been finished.

Form of materials

The three main classes of reinforcing material are glass, carbon and kevlar.

Unidirectional
Rovings are bundles of fibres which are oriented in a single direction to provide the strongest reinforcement, but only in the direction of the fibres.

Random
Chopped strand mat (CSM) is formed with strands up to 50mm long lying in random orientation. This results in the weakest laminate, but best for forming multiple curves. It provides equal strength in all directions.

Bidirectional
Woven fabrics come in quite a variety of different forms; plain, satin, twill and unidirectional weaves. Their strands are interlaced in two different directions. They may be in the form of cloth, fabric or tape, are not as strong as unidirectional fibres and may or may not give greater strength in one direction than another.

Resins

Acrylic, epoxy and polyester resins all have different advantages and snags.

Acrylic resins
Starting to compete with polyester for laminating, the main advantages of acrylic resins are their lower rate of shrinkage and minimal odour.

Figure 5.21 The excellent detail built into a commercial GRP locomotive body.

Epoxy resins
Used for high-quality composites made from glass fibres, epoxy resins are essential with carbon fibre and kevlar. Epoxy-based composites provide better impact resistance than polyester-based ones and may also produce a slightly stronger laminate. Epoxies also shrink much less than polyester resins.

Polyester resins
Polyester resin is widely used for making glass reinforced plastic. It is a strong-smelling liquid but easier to use and less expensive than epoxy resin. Polyester resins are slightly coloured and, when mixed with a catalyst, set fairly quickly. In addition gel-coat resins provide a shiny external finish which can have colour readily incorporated.

Reinforcing materials

Carbon fibre
Thin black fibres of carbon are widely used in full-size aircraft composite construction and are relatively expensive. They offer high strength, good resistance to vibration and wear as well as low friction. They are becoming increasingly used in home workshop construction where

Figure 5.22 GRP and carbon fibre are used in the construction of this working rocket.

high strength-to-weight ratios are desired and their fairly high price is acceptable.

Glass fibre
Glass fibres are exactly what their name suggests; long thin fibres of glass varying in diameter from 4 to 15μm depending on the application. As a reinforcing material, glass commonly comes as rovings, chopped strands or weaves.

Kevlar
Kevlar is chemically similar to nylon and is an aromatic polyamide fibre, first produced by Du Pont. It is renowned for its strength, light weight and resistance to stretching but is more expensive than other fibres used in composite materials. It is available in the form of cloth or as a cord.

Well known for its application to body armour, it is also suitable for making pressure vessels and rocket motor casings but, as yet, has few applications in the home workshop except where high strength and low weight are felt to be at an absolute premium.

75

CHAPTER 6

Wood

While timber is not the most popular of materials in the average model engineer's workshop, it is useful for making base boards, patterns for castings, forms over which to shape metal and as a basic raw material in models such as carriages, carts, caravans, cannon, beam engines, motor cars and railway rolling stock. It is also widely used for making handles and other tool parts, not to mention work benches and even complete workshop buildings as well as larger gauge railway sleepers, accessories and buildings.

Timber, unlike metal, is not a man-made substance with its properties carefully controlled. Partly because of this, synthetic timber products such as block board, chip board, fibre board, hardboard, MDF and plywood are increasing in popularity.

As a natural material, timber varies in consistency between samples and within individual samples. The problem of knots is a typical example of this. In addition, wood will move, particularly as humidity changes. Thus the densities given in this chapter are for air-dried timber. Some

Figure 6.1 Wood is widely used in making models which combine a mixture of different materials, like this magnificent artillery piece and limber.

types and sizes of wood are available from DIY stores and model shops, but many of the varieties are only obtainable from a specialist supplier. Some of those, which dispatch by mail order, are included in Appendix 4.

A few timbers are well known irritants. Working with mahogany or teak can cause dermatitis, while boxwood, ramin, yew and some mahogany can similarly produce eye, respiratory or skin irritation. However, bearing in mind the small amount of wood-working that is likely to take place in the average metal-working shop, this is not likely to be a significant problem.

Woods divide into two classes; hardwoods, which are not necessarily hard and softwoods, which are often hard. As an example, balsa wood, one of the softest, is a hardwood, while yew, a softwood, is harder than many hardwoods. This book only describes the limited range of woods likely to be of use in the home workshop.

Softwoods

The softwoods come from coniferous trees. There are a number of softwoods

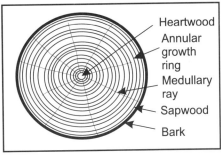

Figure 6.2 A typical cross-section of a tree.

that many people loosely and incorrectly refer to as pine. Their major applications are in the construction industry and as DIY materials. This makes them useful in workshop construction and when fitting out a building with shelves and storage units. None is suitable for external use unless it is given a significant protective coating.

Cedar

This is a light, strong, straight-grained wood which is very durable and does not warp. It has a beautiful grain which accepts a high polish. Its density is 560 kg/m³. It is used for workshop construction, boat building and pattern making.

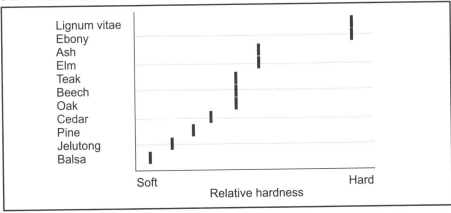

Figure 6.3 The relative hardness of various wood types helps selection of the required grade.

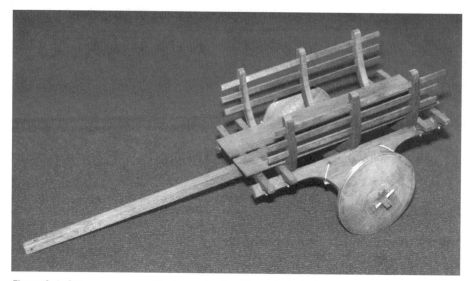

Figure 6.4 Some models need to be made virtually exclusively from wood.

Douglas fir

Also called British Columbian or Oregon pine, Douglas fir weighs 510 – 575kg/m³ and is a gold or reddish brown colour. It is a strong, durable timber that comes from trees up to 80m tall. It is available in a large range of board sizes commonly up to 200mm thick and 250mm wide, which are straight-grained. Its even texture and close grain make it easy to work, although tools require frequent sharpening. It is used in the manufacture of some plywood and it is also excellent for door frames and windows. Use oval nails as the wood is inclined to split and take care of the danger from sharp splinters.

Red Baltic or Scots pine

Grown in the UK and Northern Europe this wood is also called red pine, deal, red or yellow deal and is probably the most common softwood available. The timber is very pale yellow/cream when freshly planed but quickly darkens to a rich golden-brown on exposure to light. It shrinks a lot if used straight from the stockist. When completely dry, the timber is a pleasure to work and easy to finish. Its density is just over 400kg/m³. DIY grades may or may not be clear of knots. Red Baltic is ideal for joists, rafters, door and window frames, and floorboards if constructing or refurbishing a workshop.

Spruce

Grown in Britain, Europe and North America, its colour varies from cream to light golden yellow/brown and, as a result, it is often known as white wood. Spruce has a long, tough grain and remains much lighter in colour than redwood on exposure to light. Its density is approximately 450kg/m³ and the surface sands well. The wood is nailed or screwed easily without splitting. It is also straightforward to glue. Cut out resin pockets if possible to prevent dripping. Spruce is suitable for joinery, steps, ceilings and flooring.

78

Figure 6.5 A wooden form for a casting and the finished rotary table.

Western red cedar

Grown in Canada, its density is around 350kg/m³. Its colour lies between a pale pink/yellow and deep tan. Natural oils give the wood superb durability and stop insect attack. It is not a strong wood and its surface easily dents.

Boards are even, straight-grained with few knots. It needs very sharp tools for joint cutting but the timber machines well. One of its main uses is for making sheds. It is also used as external cladding. When left untreated outside, it turns grey as the natural oils wash out and the wood bleaches.

Yellow or white pine

Grown in North America, this is one of the softest pines. It works easily and takes a satin-smooth finish. Its density is just over 400kg/m³ and it is pale yellow when freshly cut. It changes colour quickly when exposed to light and it is rapidly ruined by damp. Because of its stability when dry, it is a popular wood for making patterns. However, it is often difficult to obtain except from specialist suppliers.

Hardwoods

The hardwoods all come from the dense close-grained wood of deciduous trees and thus provide a far greater range of different types of wood than softwood. Typical uses include tool handles, boiler cladding and bases for models such as stationary steam engines.

Ash

Grown in the UK and Europe, European ash has a density of 600 – 800kg/m³. The same tree grown in Japan is significantly less dense, softer, lighter and easier to work but unsuitable for outdoor use. A long-grained, creamy-white wood,

Figure 6.6 An ash sledge hammer handle will withstand heavy shock loads.

79

Figure 6.7 Careful timber selection is essential before starting to build up a wheel.

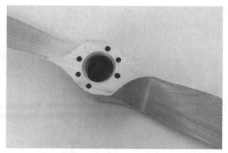

Figure 6.8 A propeller carved from beech.

ash has a coarse texture which finishes and polishes well. It is very tough and elastic making it easy to bend. The heart of the wood is brown and some timber has brown streaking. Freshly cut boards can have a pink tinge. Ash is popular for tool handles and shafts because it is able to resist sudden shock. It is used extensively in furniture and for joinery. Dried ash is easy to work and may be used indoors or out of doors.

Balsa

Originating from Latin America, balsa wood is the lightest of all commercially available hardwoods at only $160kg/m^3$. It is white or light brown in colour, sometimes with a pink hue. Its main uses are in aeromodelling but it also has a few applications in model engineering. A wide range of sheet, strip and blocks are readily available from model shops.

Basswood

American basswood, also known as American lime, is a creamy-white to pale pinkish-brown, with a straight, fine, even grain and texture. Extremely easy to work with both hand and power tools, it is an ideal carving timber which also takes stain and polishes well. Its density is around $400kg/m^3$. It is neither very strong nor durable when exposed to the elements but is popular for making forms.

Baywood

Baywood is the name originally given to quality straight-grained mahogany which grows around the bay of Honduras. It is one of the hardwoods well suited for making patterns.

Beech

Grown in Europe and UK, beech has a density of $675 - 700kg/m^3$ and is white to light brown colour. It has a straight, fine, close, even grain and even texture. Moderately hard and heavy, it is easy to work, taking screws better than most other hardwoods.

These characteristics make beech a very popular and a versatile timber. It works well and planes to a good finish but requires sharp tools. It is perfect for turning and is widely used for tools, such as mallets, and tool handles. It does not splinter but may split into a curly shape at the heart. It is unsuitable for use out of doors. Beech is an excellent material for making chairs and toys.

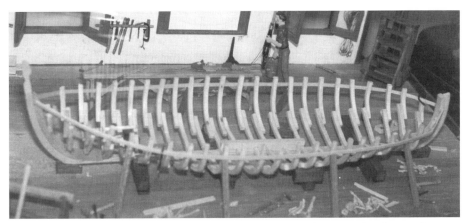

Figure 6.9 A hull under construction in the boat yard. Baywood, a type of mahogany is a popular material for the hulls of steam launches.

Birch

Birch grows in Europe and Canada and is a fairly hard, tough, strong wood which is mostly straight-grained. It has a fine, uniform texture with a light yellow colour. It is easily turned and works well to a good finish. It is widely used for flooring, mouldings and dowels, making plywood and, when treated, for external poles. Its density varies from 680 - 710kg/m³. It is one of the hardwoods used for patterns.

Ebony

This is an attractive, dense, fine, close-grained black or dark brown wood. It weighs 910 – 1100kg/m³. It is readily machined and polished to a superb finish. It is mainly used for decorative purposes and making musical instruments.

Elm

Grown in Japan, North America and the UK, Dutch elm disease decimated most trees growing in Britain. The density of elm lies in the range 525 – 725kg/m³. Coloured light brown, elms grown in the UK are tough and strongly resist splitting.

Elm is used for coffins, wheelbarrows and wooden vehicles. The wood becomes increasingly difficult to work and keep straight as it dries out. The grain of elm is often wavy but is also available with a fairly even grain. The Japanese elm is more evenly textured but less durable and tends to warp.

Hickory

This wood is the most widely employed timber for making tool handles and other applications where resilience and resistance to shock are important. It has a fine, straight, even grain and is both tough and elastic. The sapwood is a white colour, while the heartwood is red/brown. Its density is in the range 725 – 850kg/m³.

Jelutong

Jelutong comes from Southeast Asia and grows to a height of some 60m. It is a whitish-grey colour with a fine uniform texture. Its density is around 450kg/m³. The wood is straight-grained but not very durable. It is relatively soft and thus easily indented under pressure but otherwise

Figure 6.10 This is a fine way to display a stationary steam engine but requires careful selection of the right types of timber.

has good working properties. It is one of the most common hardwoods used for making patterns.

Lignum vitae

This very hard, heavy, tough and strong wood comes from the tropical regions of Central America. It darkens from a whitish yellow sapwood on its outside to greeny-brown or black in the heart. It retains its shape very well, shrinking only a little during seasoning. It requires sharp tools to achieve a hard, smooth finish. It has been widely used for slow-speed bearings and bushes as well as rollers. Its density is 1290kg/m³ and its specific gravity of 1.14 ensure it does not float. It will withstand a pressure of 72N/mm² before crushing.

Lime

Lime is a straw-coloured timber grown in the UK and Europe and has a density of around 600kg/m³. It is a fine timber for carving as it cuts cleanly in almost any direction. Its close, even grain allows the carving of exceptionally fine detail and it also turns well. It seasons rapidly and is widely available. Scrubbed and dried timber becomes white and remains smooth. Lime is unsuitable for structural or outside use.

Mahogany

Grown in the sub-tropics of America and Africa, the colour of mahogany is a quite beautiful reddish-brown. African mahogany is usually more open and cross-grained but cheaper and often stronger than wood from America. Large planks are readily

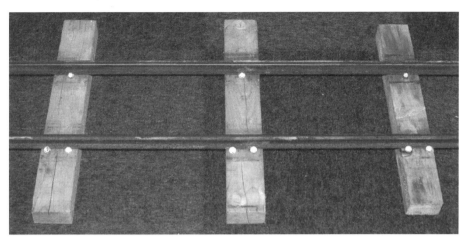

Figure 6.11 The sleepers for outside railways are best made from a wood such as oak.

available, at a price, making the use of veneer popular. American mahoganies are easier to work and more uniform in texture than the African ones and, because of the high finish achievable, have been widely used in furniture construction and pattern making. Diagonal planing of cross-grained areas often improves the finish.

Mahogany seasons well and does not easily warp but is unsuitable for outdoor use. Its density is 475 – 650kg/m³. It is widely used in small boat construction, particularly for the trim as well as for fabricating vintage aircraft propellers. It is the perfect wood for the baseboard for any static model

Maple

Maple is a tree widely grown in North America. It is hard, close-grained and is one of the hardwoods used for making patterns. It does not splinter easily and the sapwood is white, while the heart-wood is red/brown. Its density is around 640 kg/m³. It is popular for furniture and cabinet making, floors, rollers, measuring rulers and making forms.

Oak

Grown mainly in the U.K and Europe, oak has a density of 800kg/m³ and a pale beige colour which turns quickly to a light brown, then deepens slowly to a rich and often dark brown. It has a coarse, uniform texture and is usually straight-grained. The mature, inner part of an oak provides the hardest wood. Timber from trees which have grown relatively quickly has a long, straight grain and is the most suited to furniture making. Harder, short-grained timber from slowly grown trees is better for outdoor use. It is widely used for making furniture, doors, beams and fencing posts and anywhere where a hard, tough wood is required.

Figure 6.12 A block of maple and a form for a boiler end plate turned from it.

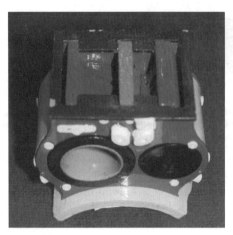

Figure 6.13 A set of patterns for a traction engine casting with each individual part painted in a different colour.

The character of oak seems to demand that it be used in reasonably large pieces: it is certainly not suitable for fine delicate work. Oak used indoors should be dry but when used outdoors, for tasks like building permanent way for model railways, it is often green and easily nails. In time, its surface will crack and it will bleach to a silvery-grey colour. Rainwater which drips from oak tends to stain anything beneath it. As iron and steel fittings corrode and they also permanently stain oak, use brass fittings instead.

Cork
Cork is the thick spongy bark which comes from a particular class of oak trees. It is a useful material for making bottle corks, and for providing insulation and vibration isolation. Although of cellular structure, it does not absorb water.

Natural cork and pressed composition cork are made into gaskets, light duty clutch linings and polishing wheels. Dried cork is very light weight, with a specific gravity of only around 0.2, and has a low thermal conductivity. It chars at 120°C, though it is quite reluctant to burn. Cork is widely available in sheet form or as tiles.

Obeche
A lightweight, straw-coloured timber grown in Africa, obeche has a density of only 320 – 380kg/m^3. It is soft and easy to work. Its dry, open grain need filling before painting and the wood soaks up quantities of stain, rapidly darkening. Worm holes are harmless as the worms die when the trees are felled.

Ramin
A hard, straw-coloured timber grown in Malaysia, ramin is close-textured, even-grained and almost knot-free. It tends to split when nailed unless a pilot hole is first drilled. It has a density of 640 – 675kg/m^3. Ramin is used widely for picture frame mouldings and is available in small rectangular planed sections but rare in large sizes. It cuts and planes well, sanding to a fine finish. Polished but unstained wood turns pale yellow.

Teak
Grown in India and Burma, teak is reddish-brown coloured and contains natural oils that make it highly resistant to decay. It is also expensive. Because of these oils, special precautions are needed before attempting to glue it. Its density is in the range 650 – 800kg/m^3.

Teak works well. as long as the tools are kept sharp. It is a tough, durable and fire-resistant wood with a long, even grain which sometimes includes an attractive black veining. Because of its resistance to damp and rot, teak is used to make items such as draining-boards, garden furniture, laboratory benches and ship's decks.

Forms of wood

As well as wood naturally cut from the trunk, there are a number of man-made, wooden materials which find a place in the home workshop. These include block board, chip board, medium density fibreboard (MDF) and plywood. Their main use lies in bases for tools and models as well as in interior fitting out of workshops. The main advantage of these synthetic timbers is their resistance to warping. Some of them are available with melamine or laminate finishes.

Blockboard
A number of strips of wood are glued side by side and faced with plywood to provide strong sheets of board. It is sold in large sheets, usually 2400mm x 1200mm and from 12.5 to 25mm thick. Ureol resin-based block board has no grain and is good for making patterns.

Chipboard
This wood-based composite is basically formed by compressing moulding chips of waste timber with urea-formaldehyde resin. It is sold in sheets of similar size to block board but may be coated with veneer or a plastic finish.

MDF (Medium density fibre board)
MDF is a close-grained composite wood material. Because it exhibits no grain, it is ideal for making patterns. It is widely sold by DIY stores in large sheets with a thickness from 2 to 50mm. It is not a waterproof material but is easily protected with paint or varnish.

Figure 6.14 A housing for a bench grinder, built from block board and ply with a polycarbonate eye shield.

Plywood
Plywood is a laminate made from a number of thin sheets of wood that are glued together with the grain of successive layers at right angles to each other. Plywood is widely available in 2400 x 1200mm sheets and is made from an odd number of layers. Thickness varies from 0.4 to 25mm.

Low-cost plywood is usually bonded together without water-resistant adhesives while marine ply uses a waterproof resin. It is not suitable for making patterns for castings. Designed to prevent warping, it is essential always to store plywood flat.

Veneer
The term veneer applies to a thin (less than 3mm) facing layer of any expensive timber which may be glued onto a base of cheap wood to provide the required artistic effect.

CHAPTER 7

Refractory and abrasive materials

Ceramic materials

Ceramics include a wide range of sub-stances such as bricks, clay, concrete, glass, refractory materials and stone. They are formed from a combination of one or more metals with a non-metallic element such as carbon, nitrogen or oxygen. The resulting materials are usually hard but brittle. They are also good electrical and thermal insulators. However, they have a low resistance to thermal shock and are easily broken if dropped or exposed to a sudden change of temperature.

For making crucibles or for making the lining of furnaces and brazing hearths, it is essential to select a material which will withstand the appropriate temperature. Materials which melt above 1580°C are called refractory while those melting above 1790°C are known as highly refractory. These materials, however, also need to resist corrosion, deformation, flaking, slag attack and softening. Their heat insulation properties are also often important.

Refractory materials are used where the ability to withstand high temperatures without significant distortion or softening are essential characteristics. Fireclay bricks, for example, for use up to 1600°C, comprise around one-third alumina and two-thirds silica. For temperatures up to

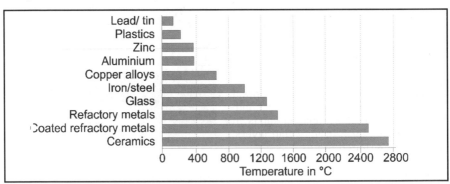

Figure 7.1 The maximum useful temperature of various materials from metals to ceramics.

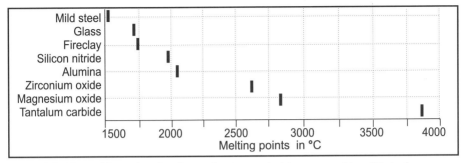

Figure 7.2 The melting point of various refractory materials compared to mild steel.

1800°C, the percentage of alumina will be increased to over 70%. Some materials will resist considerably higher temperatures but their expense and the limited requirement by model engineers for the very highest temperatures make them largely of academic interest.

Alumina

Naturally occurring aluminium oxide or alumina is a white material which also has a very high melting point and, as a key constituent of many types of clay, is used both to make bricks and as a refractory material. It is widely used for making spark plug insulators and withstands high temperatures, pressures and voltages while maintaining a gas-tight seal with the remaining parts of the plug. It is also used for lining high temperature furnaces. It melts at 2050°C.

Bentonite

A colloidal clay which swells on contact with water, Bentonite is used as a bonding clay for foundry moulding sands. It occurs in the earth in very thin layers, mainly in the United States.

Fireclay

Clays which can withstand high temperatures without cracking or melting are used for lining furnaces and making fire bricks. These clays are usually a mixture of around half each of alumina and silica and, depending on the presence of small amounts of other materials, will withstand temperatures from 870°C – 1650°C. Fire bricks made from fireclay are porous and cream-coloured. They are satisfactory up to 1500°C.

China clay, or kaolin, is white and is also used for making fire bricks and electrical insulators. It resists chipping and splintering. It does not melt until around 1700°C depending on the degree of impurities.

Figure 7.3 Spark plug insulators are made from ceramic materials to withstand the high temperatures in the combustion chamber.

Figure 7.4 A pair of sight glasses in the cab of this excellent model steam locomotive.

Glass

Most glass is made from sand, which is silica, mixed with calcium carbonate (limestone) and sodium carbonate (soda ash). Pyrex and other heat-resistant glasses have all their sodium carbonate replaced with boric oxide. Their strength depends on their chemical composition, but also on blemishes in the material and surface scratches.

Glass is brittle with a very low thermal expansion and conductivity. It is also an excellent electrical insulator that resists attack from most chemicals. Maximum service temperatures range from around 500°C – 1300°C depending on the composition of the individual piece of glass.

Perhaps the most common use of glass in the home workshop, apart from its windows, is in tube form to make water gauges for boilers. Plate glass of a reasonable thickness – 6mm and above – is a popular substitute for a surface plate. Plastic domes are available to cover clocks and they are much less prone to accidental breakage than glass. However, glass is still preferred for its optical clarity. It is also widely used to make display cases.

Glass fibres and spheres

Glass fibres 0.05 – 0.3mm in diameter are a constituent part of GRP (see page 74), while tiny glass spheres are used as

Figure 7.5 A professional glass display case.

fillers for some adhesives. Glass cloth is woven from glass fibres and is around 0.5 – 0.6 mm thick. Glass mat has the fibres intertwined in random directions. Chopped glass, with the fibres in very short lengths is useful as a filler when making GRP structures.

Chemical, electrical and thermal characteristics vary with the choice of resin, but the strength of a finished item of GRP depends on:

- The amount of glass fibre used in the items and its mechanical arrangement.
- The ratio of glass to resin.

Glass ceramic material

For making miniature spark plugs, a glass ceramic material is available which, as well as being a good insulator with low thermal conductivity, machines well to a good finish. It will withstand 800°C continuously, occasionally 1000°C and comes in rods of 6mm, 10mm and 15mm diameters.

Graphite

Some crucibles for melting gold, silver and brass, are made from graphite, a pure form of carbon. However, the graphite requires a ceramic container.

Figure 7.6 A brazing hearth needs to be lined with a refractory material.

Mica

Although not a true refractory material, mica is a fine insulator. It is, however, transparent and relatively heat resistant. It is a silicate mineral, although now rarely found as a material in its own right. Mica is still used as a filler for some plastics increasing their softening point considerably; to temperatures approaching 700°C.

Refractory cements

Most cements today are made from a mix of fireclay, silica and ganister and work up to temperatures around 1500°C. They are used to seal gaps between other forms of refractory material like bricks.

Sand

Consisting of silicon dioxide or silica, moulding sand for foundry work is fine-grained sand which is refractory and has binding qualities. It usually contains 80% or more silica to give it the necessary heat resistance and sufficient clay, up to around 15%, to bind it together, as well as a trace of iron oxide.

Material	Relative hardness	Knoop	Moh's
Glass, Crocus	Softest	300 – 600	5.5 – 6.5
Hardened steel		400 – 800	–
Quartz, Garnet		710 – 790	6 – 7.5
Emery		–	8
Aluminium oxide		1700	9
Tungsten carbide		1000 – 1500	9.09
Silicon carbide		2130 – 2140	9.15
Boron carbide		2250 – 2260	–
Cubic boron nitride		6900	10
Diamond	Hardest	7000	10

Table 7.1 An indication of the relative hardness of abrasives compared to steel.

Ganister
A particularly pure and even-grained type of silica grit, ganister, often spelled gannister, is found in northern England and used to manufacture silica bricks and refractory cements.

Silicon carbide
With a very high melting point, silicon carbide resists oxidisation well at high temperatures. It is also good at resisting thermal shock, due to its high thermal conductivity combined with its low rate of expansion. It has excellent abrasion resistance and is chemically inert. It is used to make ceramic ball and roller bearings and in the construction of high temperature furnaces.

Silicon nitride
A strong but brittle material, silicon nitride like silicon carbide, has excellent thermal shock resistance. It is found in crucibles, furnace parts, heat exchangers and high temperature bearings.

Slate and terra cotta

Purplish-grey Welsh pieces of slate or fired but unglazed tiles made from brick

clay may occasionally find application in the base for models of machinery from the Industrial Revolution.

Zirconium oxide
Also called zirconia, this hard refractory material has been widely used for many years to line high-temperature furnaces operating at up to 2500°C.

Abrasive materials

Diamond is the hardest material known to mankind and can be used to abrade any other material. There are other abrasives which are almost as hard and significantly cheaper to buy. They include both naturally occurring and man-made materials.

A polish is really just a very fine form of abrasive, which is used to provide a shiny finish on metals as well as a range of other materials such as glass and plastic.

The types of abrasives used in the home workshop comprise grinding wheels, slip, whet and oil stones, emery, sand and even harder abrasives, attached to paper or cloth, in sheet, disc and belt form, as well as the materials included in the occasional tumbling barrel.

Figure 7.7 A magnified comparison of aluminium oxide, left and silicon carbide, right shows the more angular and multi-faceted silicon carbide. (Photos courtesy CSM Just Abrasives.)

Alumina or corundum

Aluminium oxide, which is found as a natural crystalline material called corundum, is made into synthetic crystals for use as an abrasive when it is usually called alumina.

Its compressive strength and ability to resist wear means that it is used for a range of tasks including making emery paper, grinding wheels and tool tips. It is normally found with grain sizes from 100 to 600 mesh, although some coarse grinding wheels may be made from grain sizes as large as 8 mesh.

Most corundum is now manufactured from a uniform aluminium oxide. It provides an economical way of removing deep oxidation, scratches and pitting from any metal.

Ruby

Well known and prized as a gemstone, this red-coloured form of corundum also finds application, mostly today in synthetic form, as a bearing material in mechanical watches and instruments.

Cubic boron nitride – CBN

When boron carbide is compressed at a very high temperature and pressure, the material is converted into a crystal with a cubic structure which is incredibly strong and virtually as hard as diamond! It is also capable of withstanding temperatures up to just over 1900°C.

Diamond

Diamond, a crystalline form of carbon, is the hardest substance known to man. Unfortunately, it is also one of the more expensive ones. Industrial diamonds are those which are too hard, radially grained, blemished or otherwise unsuitable for making jewellery. Diamond dust comes as the refuse from cutting gem diamonds. This grit is an excellent abrasive and is available in mesh sizes from 80 right down to 60,000 and below; the latter being particles only 0.5nm across.

Emery

An abrasive powder consisting of a mix of corundum and magnetite or haemetite,

Figure 7.8 There is a wide choice of diamond-based tools for filing and finishing.

dark-brown emery occurs naturally in the countries of the north-east Mediterranean and is named after Cape Emery on the island of Naxos.

It is used as an abrasive, either ground to powder or in blocks or wheels. The grains are irregular in the natural material giving a varying grinding performance. Grains are graded in size from the finest at 220 mesh to a coarse 20 mesh.

Garnet
The name for a group of silicates, garnet finds use in abrasive papers and cloths as well as in making bearing pivots for mechanical watches.

Glass
Most glass is made from sand and is a hard but brittle material. Its hardness was widely exploited as the abrasive part of

glass or sand paper. It is still popular for smoothing rough wooden surfaces.

Pumice
Powdered or crushed volcanic pumice is widely used as the abrasive part of fine polishes. It typically contains around 75% silica, 15% alumina, 5% potash and 5% soda. It comes in a range of fine mesh sizes which are ideal for scouring metal, glass and vitreous enamels.

Sand
The hardness of sand comes from the grains of quartz it contains. Quartz or silicon dioxide is readily found on any sea shore as white, grey or yellow grains. It is used, in the form of loosely-graded grains, for sand blasting metals to remove paint and dirt or provide a rough, dull finish. It is still sometimes used as a coating of sand paper.

Quartz
Crystals of quartz generate an electric charge when subjected to pressure, and change size when exposed to an electric field. These properties are called piezo-electric. They are found in gas igniters which are better than matches for lighting brazing and gas welding torches.

Sandstone
A consolidated rock, sandstone consists of grains of sand combined with a natural cement. Usually a cream colour, it is relatively soft. Both the size of the grains of sand and the strength of the cement vary greatly and depend on the source of the stone. The most widely found sandstone is made from quartz mixed with significant amounts of clay, feldspar, lime and mica.

Silicon carbide
This man-made material is blue/black coloured and crystalline. In powdered

form, it is an excellent abrasive, widely used to make abrasive paper, cloth, wheels and hones. Grain sizes range from 60 to 1000 mesh. The grains are harder and fracture less easily than those of alumina. Silicon carbide is also used as cutting tool tips for machining metals.

Carborundum
This is a popular trade name for silicon carbide.

Tungsten carbide
This man-made iron-grey coloured powder is extremely hard (Moh's hardness above 9.5) and melts at just under 3000°C. It is used to make cutting-tool bits and as an abrasive. Tungsten carbide will sand ceramics, GRP, metal and wood.

Practical abrasives

Emery paper
Emery paper and cloth are usually graded from 24 to 1200 mesh with the grains glued to one side of 280mm x 230mm sheets. Flour of emery is the finest powder, usually dust from the crushing. Emery paper can be used dry but wet and dry paper, with a waterproof backing, is much easier to work when wetted with water.

Grinding wheels
A grinding wheel is formed of three main parts; a bonding agent, the abrasive grain and a filler. When the wheel is vitrified at high temperature, the filler burns away, leaving uniform openings throughout the wheel. The greater the amount of filler, the more porous the wheel.

Abrasives
The four main types of abrasives used to make grinding wheels grain are:

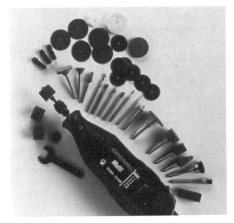

Figure 7.9 A range of abrasive tools for a mini-drill. (Photo courtesy Microflame Ltd.)

- Aluminium oxide
- Silicon carbide
- Cubic boron nitride – CBN
- Diamond

Wheels made of silicon carbide are mostly harder and stronger than aluminium oxide ones but become dull more rapidly. Diamond and CBN wheels are harder than those made of aluminium oxide or silicon carbide. In a home workshop it is normal, for cost reasons, only to find aluminium oxide or silicon carbide wheels.

Grain size
Grain is divided into four main categories depending on size. Separating screens allow smaller particles to fall through but catch larger grains, thus separating grain into different sizes.

The grain size number corresponds to the number of meshes per linear inch (yet to be metricated!) in these separating screens:

- Coarse 12 – 24
- Medium 30 – 60
- Fine 70 – 120
- Very fine 150 – 240

Figure 7.10 Grinding wheels come in a wide variety of sizes and roughness.

Bonding agents
There are five main types of bonding agents:
- Ceramic or vitrified
- Phenolic resin
- Rubber
- Shellac
- Metal

Most wheels used by model engineers are vitrified. The abrasive can either be bonded with its particles close together or with space between each individual grain. The bonding material creates a physical link between each grain.

The structure of a wheel is measured on a scale of 0 – 14, with 0 indicating a very close grain and 14 being very open with wide spacing between each grain.

Hardness
The grade or hardness of a wheel depends on the strength of the bonding. A very hard wheel holds the grains in place even against a heavy grinding force. A soft wheel releases grain from the wheel even with a light force. The amount and type of bond in a wheel determines its grade. Wheel hardness is graded alphabetically, in increasing order of hardness:
- Very soft: A – D
- Soft – medium: E - L
- Medium – hard: M – T
- Hard: U
- Very hard: V – Z

The wheels supplied with most bench grinders have a hardness classification around N, rated as hard. This class of wheel is very good for removing heavy nicks, such as those picked up by a cold chisel. However, this type of wheel will not sharpen carbide tools. Hard wheels will burn router bits and other high-speed tools.

When grinding with a soft wheel, only a small amount of material is removed, and the wheel releases grain a little at a time, presenting new cutting edges. This helps prevent the tool from overheating and produces a better edge.

For sharpening carbide-tipped cutting tools, a very hard wheel is essential. A silicon carbide wheel is ideal and these are usually a green colour, although some are black.

Bench grinders are normally supplied with two wheels, both hard grey aluminium oxide; one coarse and one fine. The two other wheels generally required for home use are a green silicon carbide wheel and a soft pink aluminium oxide one.

Material	Uses
Emery	Removing rust and scale
Tripoli	Buffing aluminium, brass, steel, pewter, bone, plastics, wood
White rouge	Giving shiny lustre to stainless steel, aluminium, iron, chrome, nickel
Red rouge	Buffing, gold, silver, platinum and other precious metals

Table 7.2 Some of the uses of the finer grades of abrasives.

Sandstones

These grind stones are quite different from those mentioned above. They are almost invariably made from natural sandstone. They run wet to avoid overheating and slowly, to avoid centrifugal stresses. They vary in grade from fine to coarse and are widely used for honing a keen edge on metal woodworking tools.

Oilstones

India oilstones were originally fine-grained blocks of dark grey emery which were impregnated with oil prior to use for sharpening metal tools.

Artificial oilstones are now also made from aluminium oxide. Arkansas oilstones are produced from silica rock, are very hard with a fine grain and are bluish-white or opaque white in colour.

Sandpaper

Although sand was originally the abrasive part of sandpaper today aluminium oxide and silicon carbide coatings are more popular. However, quartz and garnet grains are still widely used in woodworking and grades numbers are 3½, 3, 2½, 2, 1½, 0, 00 and 000.

Grit sizes typically vary from 40 to 1200, with micro-fine sizes down to 2500 and are designated as follows:
- 60 course
- 120 medium
- 180 fine

Sandpaper usually comes in sheets which measure 280mm x 230mm. The backing may be paper, cloth, fibre or web, depending on the application and, in particular, whether for hand or machine use. Fibre is used for angle grinder discs.

Steel wool

This wool is made from long thin fibres of steel and is mainly used as an abrasive or for polishing. There are as many as nine grades of steel wool, with strands varying from 0.025 to 0.1 mm diameter, usually with three edges. The thin wires are formed into flat ribbons 100mm wide and wrapped into bundles. As with any other form of steel, the quality of steel wool can vary considerably and low-priced examples may prove to be less than totally satisfactory.

Tungsten carbide

The material used as an abrasive on Permagrit® and a number of other tools, tungsten carbide powder is attached to

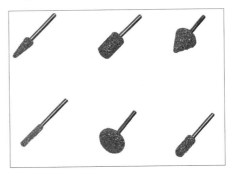

Figure 7.11 Tungsten carbide-coated rotary tools can remove material fast. (Photo courtesy Permagrit Tools.)

an aluminium block. Tungsten carbide will sand most materials; even ceramic tiles.

Valve grinding paste
By mixing aluminium oxide with thick oil or grease, a paste forms which is widely used for grinding valves into their seats.

Polishing materials

After removing material, buffing involves two further operations: first cutting down to remove scratches and surface imperfections and, second, polishing to give a final shine.

Buffing compounds
These are waxy materials which contain a very mild abrasive and remove the scratches imparted by previous abrasives. Keiselguhr is a variety of Tripoli which comes from Germany and typically contains 88% silica.

Specialist polishing compounds are available for finishing of a wide range of ferrous and non-ferrous metals as well as plastics.

Bobbing grease
This material is used for lubricating abrasive belts, abrasive-coated mops and flap wheels. It prevents dragging on softer metals like aluminium, brass and copper. It also improves the surface finish.

Emery cake
For buffing and polishing, emery cake is unlikely to be made of emery, but a graded combination of aluminium oxide and iron oxide, with a higher percentage of the hard aluminium oxide for buffing, and a larger amount of iron oxide for polishing. Emery cake is furnished in various grades

of fineness, with grains of 120 to 200 mesh, or flour sizes, F, FF, and FFF.

Lapping compounds

Rouge and crocus
Hydrated iron oxide, rouge is found in a number of shades of red colour, the darker the colour the harder the rouge. Rouge powder contains ultra-fine abrasives to provide high brilliance.

Crocus is the name applied to yellow/brown and red iron oxide powders mixed with grease to form cakes of material. Rouge and crocus are good for polishing precious metals but find little use in the home workshop apart from polishing brass and to provide optical clarity on glass.

Tripoli
This is a finely granulated, porous white mineral used as an abrasive polish and a filler. True tripoli is opaline silica, as is kieselguhr. The grains of the material are soft and porous; free of any sharp cutting edges. For this reason, tripoli is a fine polish.

Tumbling materials

Tumbling castings to improve their finish in a rotating barrel requires some form of cutting/polishing medium. This may be small, hard, round pebbles or pre-formed shapes, such as balls, cubes, cylinders or triangles made from alumina, porcelain or silicon carbide. These shapes come in a range of different sizes and those around 12.5mm are useful for polishing iron castings.

CHAPTER 8

Jointing materials

There are many ways of joining materials together. The choice depends on the items to be joined, whether they are similar or dissimilar materials, the type of joint and access to it, and whether the joint is to be a permanent or temporary one. This chapter concentrates on bonding and gluing, thread locking and retaining, as well as soldering, brazing and welding materials.

While model engineers regularly join metals using traditional techniques such as riveting, soldering or welding, modern adhesives are increasingly acceptable for many applications. Some metals and plastics are difficult to glue, making it hard to select a suitable adhesive. However, glues are popular as they avoid distortion or destruction from the application of heat. Many also enable the join to be undone by carefully applied warmth. Table 8.1 over-leaf shows the availability, strengths and weaknesses of the main adhesives used by model engineers in 1999.

The choice of adhesives

The way adhesives work falls into four main categories. Their method of working does influence their use and the first two categories below are the most useful when working with metal. The others are more applicable to working with wood.

1. Chemical setting
2. Air exclusion
3. Heat or pressure sensitive
4. Solvent, including water, evaporation or absorption

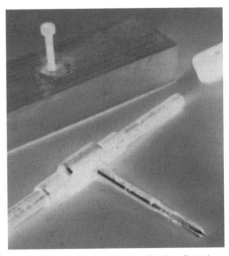

Figure 8.1 Using a filler like Rocket Powder with cyanoacrylate glue allows a filled hole to be redrilled and tapped. (Photo courtesy Deluxe Materials.)

Adhesive	Strengths	Weaknesses
Acrylic	Bonds most materials	Awkward to mix
Anaerobic	Locking threads	Needs presence of iron and air exclusion
Contact	Instant bond	Glues must be spread on both parts
Cyano	Fast setting	Needs close-fitting joint
Epoxy	Strength and gap filling	Relies on cleanliness of materials
Hot glue	Many gap-filling variants	Not for heat-sensitive applications
Plastic cement	Joins many plastics	Produces potentially hazardous fumes
Polyester	Economic GRP work	Extremely strong odour
Woodworking	Joining wood	Most not waterproof

Table 8.1 The main advantages and problems of the adhesives describes in this chapter.

Adhesives may also be placed in one of five groups depending on which type of material they are made from:

1. Natural – animal or vegetable based, including gums. Few workshop uses except for casein or latex.
2. Thermoplastic – can be softened/ melted by heat. Often brittle below 0°C. Unsuitable for use above about 65°C.
3. Elastomeric – based on natural or synthetic rubbers. Provides good flexibility but low strength, specially when heated.
4. Thermosetting – often two part, which are mixed and then cured. The best withstand 250°C.
5. Alloy adhesives – compounds of more than one chemical family.

When selecting an adhesive for a task, consider the following factors:

- The materials to be joined.
- Type of joint and the conditions it will endure.
- Any need for initial tack.
- Any limitations due to the pot and shelf lives of the adhesive.
- Time the joint takes to set.
- Strength and permanence of joint.
- The colour, cost, inflammability, smell and toxicity of the adhesive.

The form of the adhesive may also be a factor – liquid, paste, film, powder – whether it is solvent- or water-based and how it is applied. It may be used directly from the tube, with a spreader or spatula or even straight from an aerosol can.

Some adhesives are two part and must be mixed in the correct proportions before use. Others work by applying one part to one of the surfaces and the other to the second and then activating the bond by bringing the two surfaces together.

Remember that almost all adhesives depend for their adhesion on perfectly clean surfaces. This can be a particular problem with metals and plastics. Even the oils from skin can prevent a successful joint. For the best results, always roughen the surface and then clean with a solvent to remove any traces oil or grease.

The effectiveness of any adhesive will depend on factors like the temperature, the porosity of the surfaces, their fit and the load the joint will experience. Some plastic materials, like nylon, polycarbonate and polythene are particularly difficult to glue. It is only with some of the more recent formulations that any degree of success is feasible.

Caution – Most adhesives, particularly cyanos and epoxies, contain some irritant material. Take care to avoid skin and eye contact. Wash hands thoroughly after use. Keep adhesives out of reach of children.

In case of contact with eyes, always rinse immediately with plenty of water and seek medical advice.

Acrylics
These are the sole adhesives which will glue some awkward materials and they provide an immensely strong bond. The list of materials they will join includes acrylic, ABS, epoxy, metal, polyester- and epoxy-based GRP, polyester, PVC and wood. However, these adhesives will not bond to polythene or PTFE.

Acrylics have good gap-filling properties, providing a strong joint in about an hour. Apart from specialist glues like Deluxe Materials Super Crylic, whatever is being joined must be clean and grease-free.

Fast-acting variants cure in about one minute and are two-part adhesives. Apply the glue to one surface and the activator to the other prior to bringing the parts together for a rapid and permanent bond.

Anaerobics
These classic engineering adhesives are single-component liquids. They cure in the presence of iron when air is excluded from the joint. The widely-known Loctite brand consists of a wide range of anaerobics with differing characteristics for threadlocking and metal-retaining applications:

638 High strength retainer
A high strength adhesive to lock studs and other parts never to be disassembled. It will fill gaps up to 0.15mm and has a shear strength of 25 – 30N/mm^2.

601 Retainer
A high strength adhesive to retain close-fitting or press-fit parts. It will fill gaps up to 0.1mm and has a shear strength of 17.5 – 22.5N/mm^2.

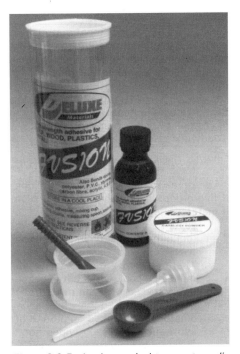

Figure 8.2 Fusion is a typical two-part acrylic adhesive. (Photo courtesy Deluxe Materials.)

270 Studlock
A medium strength adhesive for retaining bearings, bushes or oil seals. It will fill gaps up to 0.25mm and has a shear strength of 8 – 12N/mm^2.

242 Nutlock
A medium strength adhesive to prevent vibration loosening fasteners. It will fill gaps up to 0.15mm and has a shear strength of 1.5 – 4N/mm^2.

222 Screwlock
A low strength adhesive for fasteners which will be undone or adjusted later. It will fill gaps up to 0.15mm and has a shear strength of 4 – 8.5N/mm^2.

Name	Instant adhesive type	Typical bonding applications
401	General purpose	PVC seals to ABS, foam rubber strip to steel or plastic and small plastic parts to wood
406	For plastics/rubber	Silicone and nitrile rubber to plastic and for joining O-rings
4204	Tough high temperature	Plastic or metal housings for electric motors and transformers
431	General purpose	Cork to wood and plastic inserts into wood
454	General-purpose gel	Rubber to concrete, plastic to wood and rubber to aluminium
460	Low odour/bloom	Clear plastic to metal
4062	Ultra fast curing	Rubber strips to clamps, rubber ends to plastic tubes. High strength locking plastic fasteners
480	Black rubber toughened	Plastic gears to metal shafts, rubber seals to metal and ferrite magnets to plastic housings
7457	TAK PAK activator	Increasing speed of cure. Curing excess adhesive outside the bond line
770	Polyolefin primer	Priming polypropylene, polyethylene, PTFE, thermoplastic rubbers and silicones

Table 8.2 Loctite Prism superglues will meet most adhesive requirements.

Contact glues

Contact adhesives are designed to be spread on each surface and left to dry. The surfaces are then brought together to give an instant bond. These glues are ideal for joining laminates and other sheet materials. e.g. Formica and chip board.

Some of these glues are petroleum-based while others are based on latex. Examples include Copydex, which is white but dries to an almost transparent yellow, while Aero Bond is coloured so that it is evident where it has been applied. These glues are also useful for joining fabric materials both to themselves and to wood or plastic.

Cyanoacrylates (cyanos)

Superglues are single-part adhesives which provide a solid bond in seconds and give a cosmetically clean bond line. They are ideal for small, close-fitting parts made from almost any substance. Their viscosity varies from thin to gel-like.

Instant adhesives work best on clean, dry surfaces. Light abrasion of metal and plastic surfaces helps provide a key. The best bond, strongest joint and fastest cure normally results from using the minimum quantity of adhesive needed to fill the joint. The characteristics and applications of the Loctite Prism range of super-glues is shown in Table 8.2.

An activating spray speeds the curing process. It may be applied to one surface, the cyano to the other. Bringing the surfaces together provides an instant bond. Alternatively, the activator can be applied after gluing the joint. A special primer is particularly useful when working with some plastics as it allows the glue to bond to them. Fillers enable a fillet to be formed with these glues.

Always wipe the nozzle of a superglue container after use. Store unopened bottles in cool dark conditions such as a fridge. Once opened, keep the lid on when not in use. Do not refrigerate as putting the bottle back in the cold encourages condensation, quickly ruining the glue. Cyano efficiently bonds skin so keep it off fingers and other parts of the body. Debonders release glued skin and many other joined materials, but attack acrylics and polystyrene.

Epoxies
Epoxies set by chemical reaction and will survive quite high temperatures. There are many different types with varying pot lives, cure times and cured attributes. They adhere well to metals and exhibit high electrical resistance, low shrinkage, toughness and machinability. In model engineering, the most common application is as the adhesive called Araldite.

Epoxy resins are two-part glues and are among the strongest class of adhesives. They set by chemical reaction. They need a thorough mixing in the proportions specified by the manufacturer. Adhesives are available with setting times from five minutes to 24 hours at room temperature. The longer setting times give stronger bonds. Setting times can be reduced by warmth. As all epoxies emit heat when curing they should only be mixed in small quantities.

Epoxies are excellent gap-fillers and provide exceptional strength when joining metals. Heat-resistant epoxies work without failing at higher temperatures than normal epoxies. They also resist hot fuel and oil, making them suitable for some exhaust systems.

Successful epoxy joints require clean and perfectly grease-free materials. This includes finger grease. Epoxies will bond ceramics, glass, leather, metal, rubber, stone and most hard thermosetting plastics. They are not suitable for use with thermoplastics. Excess or spilled epoxy can be removed with white spirit before it has set.

Figure 8.3 Two-part epoxy glues in several setting speeds and sizes. (Photo courtesy De Luxe Materials.)

Hot glues
Hot glue is not a single type of adhesive. A range of different types of glue sticks is available, any of which can be fed into a hot-glue gun. Colourless all-purpose sticks will join materials such as brick, fabric, leather, metal, PVC, tiles and wood.

These glues only work with joints which will not be exposed to heat and where the heat of the glue will not cause damage to the materials being joined. They have excellent gap-filling capabilities and excess glue can be trimmed off with a sharp knife after it has cooled.

Coloured glue sticks, sticks with varying set times, heat resistance and viscosities are all available. Some will stick to polythene and polypropylene, while low melt ones are suitable for bonding board, fabric, film, polystyrene and plastic foams as well as wood.

Plastic cements and solvents
Solvent cements are suspensions of small particles of plastic in a suitable solvent. PVC and polystyrene cements are useful for joining these thermoplastics. Ensure good ventilation when working with them as some produce quite toxic vapours.

101

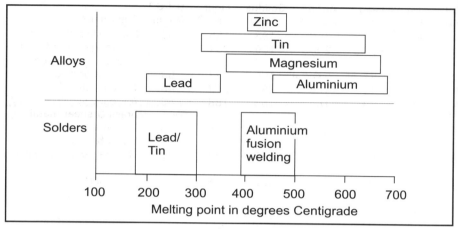

Figure 8.4 The melting points of different solders depends on the metals they contain.

Any thermoplastic can be welded with a suitable matching solvent. The melting action of the solvent means that it must be applied with care only to the joint area. The melted plastic quickly fuses before the solvent evaporates.

Polyesters

Polyester resins are normally used as the plastic part of glass reinforced plastic (GRP). They are, however, also useful for gluing wood or metal parts to completed GRP items. Good examples include the placing of formers and attachment points in GRP tram or diesel locomotive bodies.

Woodwork glues

White PVA adhesive is ideal for joining wood and comes in water-soluble and waterproof forms. It provides a slightly flexible joint which can prove difficult to sand. Standard variants provide an initial grip in about 30 minutes, although some variants only take about 10 minutes. Most brands dry completely transparent.

Aliphatic resin is a waterproof, yellow glue for joining wood, which dries faster, provides a stronger bond and is easier to sand than PVA white glue. It results in a slightly less flexible joint than PVA. Penetrating aliphatics allow assembly of wooden and some plastic joints prior to application of the glue, which then penetrates the joint in the same way as cyano.

Aerolite 306 is ideal for bonding laminated plastics, like formica, to wood. A two-part glue, one part is applied to each surface and the two parts are then brought together to provide a strong, heatproof and waterproof joint.

Solders, brazing alloys, welding rods and fluxes

There are many different products on the market for use when joining a variety of metals at different temperatures. While most steel, copper and brass are relatively straightforward to join; aluminium and stainless steel have historically proved difficult but are now little harder than other metals. Borax is used as a flux when soldering or melting many metals.

BS type	Tin %	Lead %	Antimony %	Solidus °C	Liquidus °C	U.T.S.* N/mm²	Comments
A	63	36	0.6	183	185	60	For capillary/fine joints
B	49/59	38/48	2.5/3	185	204	60	(Stronger than F & R, (but do not use on (brass or zinc
C	40	57	2.0/2.4	185	227	53	
F	50	49	0.5	183	212	46	Cheaper than K
K	60	39	0.5	183	188	59	All-round solder. For zinc brass & sheet metal
M	45	53	2.2/2.7	185	215	56	R with antimony, for brass & zinc
R	45	54	0.4	183	224	43	General solder, cheaper than F
W	15	84	0.2	183	276	–	Good surface filler, suitable for low temps.
95A	95	–	5	236	243	20	High temperature
5S †	5	93.5	–	290	300	19	High temperature

† contains 1.5% silver   * with gaps of 0.05 – 0.15mm.

Table 8.3 The composition and characteristics of a range of soft solders, including some high temperature ones.

Tin/lead-based solders

Tin and lead, with their low melting points, are widely used to make soft solders which will liquefy from 180°C to 300°C. Details of the contents and melting range are given in Table 8.3. Readily melted by a soldering iron or a naked flame, they are only suitable for making lightly-stressed joints. When dealing with folded sheet metal work, soft solder provides a leak-proof joint and is widely used for joining brass, copper and tin plate. Solder for electronic work includes a resin-based flux within hollow cores in the solder.

Aluminium solders

Aluminium is difficult to solder because it oxidises so rapidly. Fusion welding with a suitable solder has solved this problem for aluminium and its alloys. It is effective at a temperature around 200°C below the melting point of aluminium.

It works with most aluminium alloys including Mazaks, magnesium and high zinc content alloys. Neither flux nor an inert gas envelope are needed. Joints resist salt water corrosion and can be machined, drilled or tapped. It is suitable for all types of joint from very thin to thick sections.

Material data	Technoweld	Lumiweld
Working temperature	392°C – 495°C	382°C – 491°C
Tensile strength	Exceeds 345N/mm²	–
Shear strength exceeds	310N/mm²	–
Solidification shrinkage	1.2%	1.2%
Brinell hardness	97	100
Density	6.7g/cu.cm @ 21°C	6.92g/cu.cm

Table 8.4 The key characteristics of two popular aluminium solders.

Name	Ag %	Cd	Solidus °C	Liquidus °C	Also contains	Gap filling in mm
AG1	50	✓	620	640		0.025 - 0.1
AG2	42	✓	610	620		0.05 - 0.1
AG3	38	✓	605	650		0.05 - 0.15
AG5	43	x	690	770		0.075 - 0.2
AG9	50	✓	635	655	Nickel	Applied as foil.
AG11	34	✓	610	670		0.075 - 0.2
AG12	30	✓	600	690		0.1 - 0.2
AG13	60	x	695	730		0.05 - 0.15
AG14	55	x	630	660	Tin	0.05 - 0.125
AG18	49	x	680	705	Nickel, Manganese	Applied as foil.
AG20	40	x	650	710	Tin	0.05 - 0.2
AG21	30	x	665	755	Tin	0.05 - 0.2

Table 8.5 The properties of some popular current silver solders.

It is also worth noting that aluminium can successfully be joined with most lead-free soft solders.

Silver solders

High-melting-point solders are used for joints where the strength of soft solders is insufficient. Most of them are made

Figure 8.5 Silver solder is the perfect material to use when making a copper boiler, providing strength as well as steam-proof joints.

from silver, copper and zinc; the inclusion of silver significantly affecting the price due to its high cost. Small amounts of tin, manganese and nickel may also be incorporated. Some of these solders still contain cadmium and require care about ventilation when working with them, as they can emit poisonous fumes.

A range of melting temperatures enables multiple soldering without initial joints melting when subsequent ones are made. The popular British Standard grades of silver solder, their melting ranges and gap-filling capabilities are shown in Table 8.5.

Brazing rods

These rods are basically made from brass, which melts at around 880°C and are commonly called spelter. Their advantage lies in their low cost when compared with silver solder. Their snag is their higher melting temperature, but they are still worth using when joining steel or copper.

Table 8.7 shows the approximate constituents of a number of popular brazing rods together with their melting points. The actual amounts will vary within specified limits and will depend on the particular manufacturer.

| Name | Trade names | | | Uses |
	Johnson Matthey	Fry's Metals	Thessco	
AG1	Easyflo No 1	No 3	MX20	Better flow & corrosion resistance than AG2
AG2	Easyflo No 2	No 2	MX12	General-purpose solder
AG3	Argoflo	No 1	AG3	For forming fillets
AG5	Silverflo 43	No 5		For forming fillets
AG9	Easyflo No 3	No 19	MX20N	Attaching carbide tips
AG11	Mattibraze 34	No 15	MX4	Forming fillets
AG12	Argoswift	No 16	MX.O	Gap filling & fillets
AG13	Silverflo 60	No 4	HO	Working with nickel
AG14	Silverflo 55	No 29	M25T	Cadmium-free version AG1
AG18	Argobraze 49H	No 37	M19MN	Working with cast iron
AG20	Silverflo 40		M10T	) Low cost, wide
AG21	Silverflo 302	No 33	MOT	) melting range

Table 8.6 Silver solder trade names from three major manufacturers.

Welding rods

There are various types of continuous feed wire and rod made from different materials. The most common are copper-coated soft iron or mild steel wire from 0.6mm to 1mm diameter, although sizes range up to 6mm. Flux-cored welding rod, aluminium welding rod and stainless steel welding rod are also available for use with different metals. For use when arc welding, the electrode is typically flux-coated wire in one of seven diameters from 1.6mm to 7mm.

Fluxes

In soldering, brazing and welding, the only purpose of flux is to remove oxides from the surface of the metal being joined. This allows the solder, brazing or welding rod to flow freely. There are specialist fluxes to suit most materials and temperatures.

Acid-based fluxes

These are the standard fluxes for use when soft-soldering metal work. Due to their corrosive nature, the residues of flux should be cleaned away after soldering. Baker's fluid is a popular brand. Acid-based fluxes should never be used when making electrical or electronic joints.

Aluminium fluxes

To avoid the formation of a protective skin on aluminium, these fluxes are, by their very nature, corrosive and must be removed with warm water after soldering.

Brazing fluxes

The most common material used as a flux when brazing is powdered borax, preferably in its anhydrous form. It will perform satisfactorily at temperatures up to 1000°C.

Name	Cu	Zn	Sn	Si	Mn	Ni	Solidus °C	Liquidus °C
CZ6	60%	39.5%	0.2%	0.3%			875	895
CZ7	60%	39.3%	0.2%	0.3%	0.2%		870	900
CZ8	50%	39.3%	0.2%	0.3%	0.2%	10%	920	980

Table 8.7 The constituents and melting range of some widely used brazing rods.

Resin-based fluxes

In the form of non-corrosive pastes, resin-based fluxes are specially designed for use when making joints in electrical and electronic equipment. A widely used brand is Fluxite, that is available from most companies which supply electronic components.

Self-cleaning fluxes

These water-soluble fluxes have been specially produced to completely eliminate the need to sand or clean copper pipe before soldering it. They are easily flushed away when the job is finished.

Sifbronze flux

Often known just as Sif flux, Sifbronze flux works extremely well as a general-purpose flux for brazing and welding many metals.

Silver-solder fluxes

Each manufacturer recommends a flux for use with each different grade of silver solder. Fluoride-based fluxes work across the temperature range 550°C – 750°C. For higher temperatures, flux is usually a mix of fluorides and borates. These powders need mixing to a pasty consistency before application.

Stainless steel fluxes

Soldering stainless steel is never a simple process and a special active flux is essential to ensure a satisfactory joint.

Tippex

Typist's correcting fluid can prevent metal surfaces getting covered with solder or spelter when brazing. It is removed with its own thinners. Tippex is a suspension of white solid in trichlorethane.

CHAPTER 9

Cleaning, etching, pickling and plating fluids

Cleaning, etching and pickling

This first section deals with chemicals used as constituents of solutions for cleaning, etching and pickling metals. A list of the basic chemicals is followed by details of solutions to suit various tasks. **Caution** – Some liquids are acids, while others are very alkaline. Both are highly corrosive. Wear goggles, overalls and gloves when working with them and avoid splashing the liquids. Always slowly add acid to water, never the other way round, stirring continuously to avoid overheating. Chemicals considered too dangerous for use in home workshops are excluded.

Acetic and citric acids
Vinegar is a readily available source of 3% – 6% acetic acid in water, together with some other impurities. Citric acid, now prepared commercially, naturally occurs in many fruit, most notably in lemons. Citric acid can be purchased from wine-making shops. Both acids are safe if slow pickles for cleaning metals.

Ferric chloride
A brown, crystalline and lumpy material, ferric chloride is soluble in warm water and was widely used for the etching of copper-clad printed circuit boards. It has largely been replaced for this task by sodium persulphate. Ferric chloride is also a fine etchant for aluminium, copper and steel, including stainless steel.

Hexamine
A white crystalline powder made from formaldehyde and ammonia, hexamine readily dissolves in water and is also known as formin and ammonio formaldehyde. It is used as an inhibitor in acid pickle.

Hydrochloric acid
Originally known as spirits of salts, hydrochloric acid gas dissolved in water is a colourless or yellow fuming liquid. When the liquid contains more than about a third gas, it gives off pungent poisonous fumes. It is used for pickling and cleaning metal and in flux for soldering zinc.

Hydrogen peroxide
Looking like water, hydrogen peroxide contains an additional oxygen atom and is widely used for bleaching and oxidising. It is also used as a constituent of a bright dip for aluminium. It is available in various percentage strengths dissolved in water.

Nitric acid

Also known as aqua fortis, nitric acid is a highly corrosive acid which varies in colour between clear and slightly red. Soluble in water, any solution in water containing over 86% acid is known as fuming nitric acid. Its fumes have a suffocating action. It is widely used for colouring anodised aluminium and both as a pickle and an etchant for metals.

Phosphoric acid

A colourless, syrupy liquid which is soluble in water, phosphoric acid is used to pickle metals and provides a slight etch on aluminium, steel and zinc. It is available as a descalant from plumbers' merchants.

Sodium carbonate

Also commonly called soda ash, sodium carbonate is a white/grey lumpy material which normally contains some water and is widely available as washing soda or soda crystals and used for its cleansing properties. It is good for cleaning metals. It is **not** the same as baking soda which has a different chemical formula.

Sodium fluoride

This white powder, soluble in water, is popular as a wood preservative but is also a constituent of aluminium pickle.

Sodium hydroxide (caustic soda)

Sodium hydroxide is a white crystalline solid which is soluble in water and is used for scouring and cleaning domestic baths and for cleaning metals, particularly aluminium. It is also found in cutting and soluble oils. It is a caustic material and is likely to cause skin irritation.

Sodium trisilicate

This powerful detergent is a water soluble powder and is used in alkaline metal cleaners. It is often referred to as water glass and is widely used in the making of industrial adhesives.

Sulphuric acid

This highly corrosive, oily liquid is yellow/brown in colour. It mixes with water and is widely used for cleaning metals and in batteries.

Battery acid is 33% sulphuric acid in distilled water. Diluting it – one part by volume of battery acid to two by volume of distilled water produces 10% sulphuric acid; one part by volume of battery acid to one and a half by volume distilled water to give 12% sulphuric acid; a mix of one part acid to 1.1 parts by volume of distilled water gives 15% sulphuric acid.

When adding the acid to water, stand plastic containers in outer tank of cold water. Ensure good ventilation as some dipping produces hazardous fumes.

Cleaners

Any cleaning solution is one that is used to remove traces of flux, grease, oil and residual polish compounds from metal components.

Alkaline cleaner for ferrous metals, copper and its alloys

Solution:	40g sodium hydroxide
	25g sodium carbonate
	25g sodium trisilicate
	1 litre water
Tank:	Steel

Alkaline cleaner for aluminium and zinc die castings

Solutions:	20g sodium hydroxide
	25g sodium carbonate
	1 litre water
Tank:	Plastic, steel or glass

Etchants

Chemicals used to dissolve, cut or etch the surface of metals, and other materials are often acid based. There are, however, alternatives.

The remaining surface of the item being etched may be protected with a layer of wax. The following etchants are suitable for use in the home workshop:

Material	Solution
Steel	Ferric chloride
Stainless steel	Ferric chloride and hydrochloric acid in water
Brass	Nitric and hydrochloric acid together in water
Copper	Ferric chloride
Aluminium	20% ferric chloride

Pickles and bright dips

Pickling metals uses acids to clean them by removing impurities such as scale and rust from the surface with little attack or removal of the actual metal beneath the impurities. It is also a prerequisite to the electroplating process. The constituents of the pickle will depend on which metal is to be cleaned.

Be very careful if using concentrated acid. It should be possible to purchase dilute acid of the correct strength or, if still too strong, to weaken it further by slowly adding it to water.

For those who are unhappy to use the concentrated acids listed in the pickles below, either acetic acid or citric acid is an acceptable substitute, both of which are perfectly safe to handle. Both may be used neat but will take much longer to clean the metal than other pickles.

Acid pickle for iron, steel, copper and its alloys

Solution:	50ml concentrated sulphuric acid, 950ml water. Or 100ml concentrated sulphuric acid, 900ml water. Or 150ml concentrated sulphuric acid, 850ml water. Or 200ml concentrated hydrochloric acid, 800ml water.
Mixing:	Slowly pour acid into half water, stirring continuously as mixing generates plenty of heat. Add remaining water.
Tank:	Plastic or glass.

Inhibited acid pickle to remove scale from ferrous materials

Solution:	200ml concentrated hydrochloric acid, 800ml water. 5g hexamine.
Mixing:	Slowly pour acid into half water, then add remaining water. Add hexamine, stirring to dissolve.
Tank:	Plastic or glass.

Aluminium and its alloys pickle

Solution:	250ml concentrated nitric acid, 10g sodium fluoride, 750ml water.
Mixing:	Slowly pour acid into half water, stirring continuously. Add sodium fluoride. Stir to dissolved. Add remaining water.
Tank:	Plastic or glass.

Bright dip for copper, its alloys and nickel silver

Solution:	500ml concentrated sulphuric acid, 185ml concentrated nitric acid, 15ml concentrated hydrochloric acid, 300ml water.
Mixing:	Slowly add sulphuric acid to water, stirring continuously as mixing generates plenty of heat. Allow solution to cool to room temperature. Stirring continuously, add nitric acid, then hydrochloric acid.
Rinse:	12g sodium carbonate per litre of cold water.
Tank:	Plastic, glass or stainless steel.

Bright dip for aluminium

Solution:	440ml concentrated phosphoric acid, 4ml hydrogen peroxide (20 volumes), 21ml water.
Mixing:	Slowly add acid to water, stirring continuously. Allow solution to cool. Add hydrogen peroxide.
Rinse:	Cold water.
Tank:	Plastic or glass.

Jenolite
A phosphoric acid based pre-treatment, Jenolite is applied to steel before painting.

Electroplating

Electroplating is useful for several tasks. It is perfect for protecting metals which corrode by plating them with a coat of corrosion-free metal. It is useful for decorative purposes and can give a metallic look to plastics.

It can also provide a thin layer of expensive metal on low-cost (or stronger) metal objects. Plated items are usually dull, but most can be buffed and polished.

This section lists the wide range of chemicals used to make up the various plating solutions and then provides details of the proportions used in the various solutions themselves. It excludes those too dangerous for home use.

Ammonia
Water at room temperature absorbs as much as 680 times its own volume of ammonia gas to form a liquid commonly called ammonia but actually ammonium hydroxide. It is a colourless but pungent liquid which is very alkaline. It is used in solutions for the coloured anodising of aluminium and is also an excellent bleach and cleaning agent. Soaking wood in ammonia makes it much easier to bend.

Ammonium chloride
Also known as sal ammoniac, ammonium chloride is a white crystalline powder which is a constituent of some zinc plating solutions. It is also used to make some solder fluxes.

Ammonium molybdate
This salt of molybdic acid is a component of the solution for black anodising aluminium. It is also poisonous. It comes as colourless or yellow crystals which are soluble in water to form an acidic solution.

Boric acid
This white crystalline powder is soluble in water and is a valuable flux, used when soldering and brazing. It also used in nickel plating and electroforming solutions.

Figure 11.1 A plating bath made from a polythene container and copper rod. The part being plated is seen hanging from the central rod while above it is one of the two sacrificial anodes.

Copper sulphate
This common sulphate of copper is a blue crystalline lumpy material (a white powder in its anhydrous form) and is soluble in water. It is used in solutions for colour anodising aluminium and electroplating copper.

Dextrin
This is a white, sweet-tasting powder which dissolves in water to form a syrupy liquid. It is widely used in making pastes for use on postage stamps and envelopes and also as an additive to zinc plating solutions

Distilled or de-ionised water
Distilled water is water which has had impurities removed by a process of distillation. De-ionised water, on the other hand, has had impurities removed by the very different ionic process.

Double nickel salt
This is another name for nickel ammonium sulphate, which is used industrially for plating a harder and whiter nickel finish on zinc, but is also a constituent of solutions used for anodising aluminium brown.

Ferric chloride
As described on page 107, this brown, crystalline material is soluble in warm water. It is used in pre-plating solutions for aluminium.

Hydrochloric acid
As previously mentioned on page 107, hydrochloric acid gas dissolves in water to form a colourless or yellow fuming liquid. When the liquid contains more than about a third gas, it gives off pungent poisonous fumes. It is used for electroless tin plating.

Nickel chloride

This green crystalline salt is used with boric acid, when nickel plating, to give a smooth, hard, fine-grained result.

Nickel sulphamate

Formed from the reaction of black nickel oxide and sulphanic acid, nickel sulphamate is used in electroless nickel plating and is very soluble in water.

Nickel sulphate

This is the most widely used material for nickel plating and is also called single nickel salt. It is available as bright-green crystalline pellets which are soluble in water. However, some care is necessary as it readily converts to sulphuric acid.

Nitric acid

As described on page 108, nitric acid is a very corrosive acid; soluble in water. A solution containing over 86% acid is called fuming nitric acid. Its fumes have a suffocating action. It is used in solutions for colouring anodised aluminium.

Phenol

Also called carbolic acid, phenol improves the grain of electroformed copper.

Potassium chlorate

Also referred to as chlorate of potash, potassium chlorate is an odourless, white, crystalline powder which is used when colouring anodised aluminium.

Potassium hydroxide (caustic potash)

A white, lumpy material which dissolves in water, it has very similar properties to sodium hydroxide but is more expensive. It is used in tin electroplating solutions.

Potassium stannate

The commercial product is the trihydrate and is a white crystalline powder which is soluble in water to form an alkaline solution. It is used for tinning aluminium.

Rochelle salt

Rochelle salt is the name for potassium sodium tartrate, a colourless/bluish white crystalline substance. It is dissolved in water and is a constituent of solutions for pre-electroplating aluminium.

Sodium acetate

Available as anhydrous or 60% trihydrate grades, sodium acetate is either a white hygroscopic powder or crystalline in form. Both are soluble in water and used for electroless nickel plating.

Sodium dichromate

This red crystalline powder is used to provide colour when anodising aluminium.

Sodium hydroxide (caustic soda)

As previously mentioned on page 108, sodium hydroxide is a white crystalline solid which is soluble in water and is used in zinc electrolytes. It is a caustic material which need careful handling because it causes skin irritation.

Sodium hypophosphite

A soluble white solid formed when hypophosphorous acid reacts with sodium carbonate, the liquid is then evaporated to leave a solid residue. It is used for electroless nickel plating.

Stannous chloride

Available as white, water-soluble flakes, it is widely used in tin plating processes. It also comes as large colourless crystals which are not suitable for this purpose.

Stannous sulphate

This sulphate of tin is a white crystalline powder which is soluble in water. It is used for electroless tin plating.

Sulphuric acid

As mentioned on page 108, this is a very corrosive liquid. In concentrated form, it is used in electroplating. When adding to water, stand plastic containers in tank of cold water. Ensure good ventilation as some plating gives off hydrogen gas.

Thiourea

These white crystals are water soluble and used in copper and electroless tin plating. Thiourea is also called sulphocarbamide, sulphourea and thiocarbamide.

Zinc chloride

This white, crystalline, soluble powder is used in solutions for electroplating zinc.

Zinc oxide

Zinc oxide is a fine white powder, used in paints and rubbers and even protective sun creams. It is also a constituent of zinc plating solutions.

Zinc plating

Zinc plating is one of the best ways of providing protection from corrosion for ferrous and non-ferrous metals. The zinc chloride electrolyte shown below works particularly well with steel and will even plate more awkward metals such as cast iron. It is also safer to work with than the zinc hydroxide electrolyte.

Zinc chloride electrolyte for zinc plating

Solution:	20g zinc chloride, 120g ammonium chloride, 1 litre tap water.
Mixing:	Add ammonium chloride to 750ml water. Stir to dissolve.
	Add zinc chloride to separate 250ml warm water. Stir to dissolve.
	Mix solutions together well. Mark liquid level on outside of tank.
	Keep covered and replace water lost through evaporation.
Anode:	Zinc or perforated zinc sheet.
Tank:	Pyrex glass, plastic or stainless steel.

Zinc hydroxide electrolyte for zinc plating

Solution:	6g zinc oxide, 55g sodium hydroxide, 1 litre water, 1g dextrin.
Mixing:	Add sodium hydroxide to 750ml water. Stir to dissolve.
	Add zinc oxide and stir until dissolved. Added dextrin and stir to dissolve. Make up volume to 1 litre with water.
Anode:	Zinc or perforated zinc sheet.
Storage:	Sealed plastic or glass jar.
Tank:	Plastic, pyrex glass or stainless steel.

Coloured zinc plating

Colouring zinc electroplating is known as passivating the zinc surface. It is a decorative process with a variety of colours and enhances the performance of the electrolyte by increasing its anti-corrosive properties. Brown or iridescent coloured ferrous metals can be painted to provide a high level of corrosion resistance.

Zinc, along with cadmium, is classed as a sacrificial coating on ferrous materials. This means that over a period of years the electroplated deposit will be oxidised instead of the component becoming rusty due to the formation of iron oxide.

However, over a period of a few years the electroplated deposit will disappear from the coated component. To reduce the activity of this deposit, a passive layer is applied to it, usually of chromium. This effectively reduces the activity and thus prolongs the life of the deposit. It also actively enhances the anti-corrosive properties of the coating.

Black

Solution:	25g per litre ammonium molybdate, 37.5ml concentrated ammonia (.880 SG), 937.5ml water.
Mixing:	Dissolve ammonium molybdate in water. Slowly add ammonia, stirring well.
	For deep black, heat solution – ammonia will fume and smell pungent.
Rinse:	Cold then hot water. Leave to harden.
Tank:	Pyrex glass, plastic or stainless steel.

Brown

Solution:	3g double nickel salt, 3g copper sulphate, 3g potassium chlorate (store in sealed container), 1 litre water.
Mixing:	Add nickel salts, copper sulphate and potassium chlorate to water. Stir to dissolve.
Tank:	Plastic, pyrex glass or stainless steel.

Blue

Solution:	5g sodium dichromate. 20ml concentrated nitric acid, 1 litre water.
Mixing:	Dissolve sodium dichromate in water. Slowly add acid, stirring well.
Tank:	Plastic, pyrex glass or stainless steel.

Iridescent colour

Solution:	60g sodium dichromate, 3ml concentrated sulphuric acid, 1 litre water.
Mixing:	Dissolve sodium dichromate in water.
	Slowly add acid, continuously stirring.
Tank:	Pyrex glass, plastic or stainless steel.

Copper plating

No details are provided of copper plating using cyanide, due to the hazards and difficulty in obtaining cyanide. Two copper electrolytes are detailed which will plate non-ferrous metals. Ferrous metals must first be electroplated with nickel, rinsed and while wet, immersed in the copper electrolyte.

Dull copper electrolyte for copper plating

Solution:	200g copper sulphate crystals, 30ml concentrated sulphuric acid, 1 litre water.
Mixing:	Add copper sulphate to 750ml warm water. Stir to dissolve. Cool soluution, slowly add acid and stir well to mix. Slowly add remaining water.
Anodes:	Purified copper (phosphorised).
Tank:	Pyrex, plastic glass or stainless steel.

Semi-bright copper electrolyte for copper plating that can be buffed and polished

Solution: 200g copper sulphate, 27ml concentrated sulphuric acid, thiourea 0.005g (a pinch), 1ml wetting agent (Teepol), 1 litre water.

Mixing: Add copper sulphate crystals to 750ml warm water. Stir constantly to dissolve. Cool solution and slowly add acid. Stir well to mix. Slowly add remaining water and then the thiourea and wetting agent.

Anodes: Purified copper (phosphorised).

Tank: Stainless steel or plastic/rubber lined steel.

Nickel plating

Nickel plating provides good corrosion resistance on ferrous and non-ferrous metals. Pre-cleaning is, however, essential to avoid surfaces with pores or other discontinuities.

Watt's nickel is a really excellent plating solution and can be over-electroplated with decorative chrome to give a dull chrome effect.

To achieve a semi-bright finish requires the addition of 2.0g of ordinary saccharine to the solution.

Watt's nickel for nickel plating

Solution: 240g nickel sulphate, 45g nickel chloride, 30g boric acid, 1 litre water.

Mixing: Add nickel sulphate to 750ml warm water, Stir and warm to dissolve. Add nickel chloride. Stir and warm to dissolve. Add and dissolve boric acid. Add further 250ml water.

Anodes: Pure nickel.

Tank: Stainless steel, pyrex glass or plastic

Tin plating

Tin plating prevents corrosion on ferrous and non-ferrous metals. It is used as a decorative finish and to facilitate soldering. It gives a light grey, matt finish, which can be buffed to a silvery finish. Tin-plating crystals, for use on printed circuit boards, can be purchased from electronic component companies.

Electroplating aluminium, ceramics and plastics

Aluminium cannot be electroplated like other metals, and non-conductors must first be made electrically conductive with a layer of silver-loaded conductive paint. Some are just painted on and left to dry, others suitable for ceramics, can be fired.

Potassium stannate electrolyte for tin plating

Solution: 95g potassium stannate, 12g potassium hydroxide, 1 litre distilled or de-ionised water.

Mixing: Add potassium stannate to 750ml warm water. Stir continuously to dissolve. Add potassium hydroxide, stirring until dissolved. Add remaining water.

Tank: Pyrex glass, plastic, mild or stainless steel.

Zincate solution for preparing aluminium for plating

Solution:	440g sodium hydroxide, 87g zinc oxide, 1 litre water. For a more even deposit add 0.5g ferric chloride crystals, 5g rochelle salt.
Mixing:	Slowly add sodium hydroxide to 500ml water. Stir continuously to dissolve. While warm, add zinc oxide. Stir to dissolve. Add remaining water and allow to cool.
Rinse:	Water.
Tank:	Pyrex, glass or plastic.

After cleaning, immerse aluminium in zincate solution and, while wet, place in Watt's nickel electrolyte (see page 115) to deposit 0.005mm of nickel. After rinsing, it can be readily coated with other metals.

Electroless or chemical plating solutions

These solutions are based on a chemical containing the metal to be deposited, in water, and a similar solution of a reducing agent. These two are then mixed to form an electroless plating solution; the component itself acting as a catalyst.

Electroless nickel

Nickel can be plated onto aluminium, ferrous metals, copper and its alloys using iron or aluminium wire as a catalyst.

Tin electroless plating

This process provides a thin layer of tin over all ferrous metals, copper and its alloys. To pre-clean printed circuit boards prior to immersion in the plating solution, rub lightly with scouring powder and rinse.

Electroless nickel plating solution

Three separate solutions:	30g nickel chloride crystals, 1litre water. 10g sodium hypophosphite, 1 litre water. 50g sodium acetate crystals, 1 litre water.
Mixing:	Add each constituent to a separate litre of water. Store separately in glass bottles. For plating, mix sufficient of the three solutions together.
Tank:	Pyrex glass.

Electroless tin for iron and steel

Solution:	Stannous sulphate 1.5g, concentrated sulphuric acid 4ml, 995ml water.
Mixing:	Slowly add acid to water, continuously stirring; then dissolve stannous sulphate.
Tank:	Heat-resistant glass or plastic

Electroless Tin for copper and its alloys

Solution:	l0g stannous chloride, 85g thiourea, 15ml concentrated hydrochloric acid, 900ml water.
Mixing:	Slowly add acid to water, continuously stirring; then dissolve stannous chloride and thiourea.
Tank:	Heat-resistant glass or plastic

116

Electroforming copper and nickel

The process of electroforming allows metal to be deposited on a suitable form. Either pure copper or nickel may be electroformed into intricate shapes. The amount of metal deposited is normally from 0.3mm to 2mm.

Copper electroforming electrolyte

Solution:	200g copper sulphate crystals, 30ml concentrated sulphuric acid, 1 litre water. A small amount of phenol, dissolved in water, refines the grain.
Mixing:	Add copper sulphate crystals to 750ml warm water. Stir constantly to dissolve. Cool solution and slowly add acid. Stir well to mix. Slowly add remaining water.
Anodes:	Purified copper (phosphorised).
Tank:	Pyrex, plastic glass or stainless steel.

Nickel electroforming electrolyte

Solution:	450g nickel sulphamate, 30g boric acid, 1 litre water.
Mixing:	Add nickel sulphamate to 750ml warm water. Stir and warm to dissolve. Add and mix boric acid. Add remaining water.
Tank:	Pyrex glass, stainless steel or plastic.

Anodising solutions

Anodising is a process which is applied to aluminium and its various alloys. It uses sulphuric acid to provide an attractive layer of protection which may also be coloured.

Most aluminium alloys can be anodised, but the purer the aluminium the better the resulting anodised film. The thickness of the barrier layer depends on the voltage used during the plating process while the pore size depends on the acid concentration, temperature and current.

Aluminium alloy constituents, such as silicon and manganese, will retard the anodising process and certain alloys and some castings do not anodise well. The three sulphuric acid concentrations that are practical for anodising are shown below.

Anodising solution for treating aluminium

Solution:	**For hard films with small pore size**: 10% volume sulphuric acid, 90% volume distilled/deionised water.
	General purpose: 12% volume sulphuric acid, 88% volume distilled/deionised water.
	For larger pore size suitable for dyeing: 15% volume sulphuric acid, 85% volume distilled/deionised water.
Mixing:	Slowly add acid to water, constantly stirring.
Cathodes:	2 pieces clean sheet lead on opposite sides of tank.
Anode:	Components to be anodised. Connect with aluminium wire.
Sealing:	Use boiling deionised water.
Tank:	Glass or polythene.

Dyeing anodised aluminium

Most aluminium alloys are silver when anodised. However, any alloy containing 5% – 8% copper, silicon, manganese, or magnesium will colour the anodisation; orange/yellow for copper content, brown for those containing manganese, and blue/grey for magnesium- or silicon-based alloys. For other colours, organic dyes may be used.

Dyeing solution for colouring aluminium

Dye:	1g – 10g per litre of water depending on shade required.
Mixing:	Add dye to half a litre of hot water. Stir until dye has dissolved. Add further half litre of cold water and adjust temperature.
Rinse:	In cold water before and after dyeing.
Tank:	Quality stainless steel, plastic or glass.

CHAPTER 10

Coatings, fuels, lubricants and other workshop materials

Coatings – paint, varnishes and solvents

The effects of corrosion, particularly rust on ferrous metals and damp on wooden materials, have resulted in the development and refinement over the years of a wide variety of paints, varnishes and other similar coatings.

Paints consist of solutions of pigment in water, oil or some other solvent. They are used to cover wood, metal or other materials for protection or to improve their appearance. Spray painting always gives a better result than a hand-brushed finish and many home workshops boast an air brush or spray gun. However, the finish achieved will depend not only on surface preparation but also on using the correct undercoats.

Not all paints are compatible and the wrong combination can result in bubbles spoiling the finish. A basic rule is never to put cellulose on top of enamel. If doubtful, test a sample first. As most paints take some time to harden completely, it is important to be patient between coats. A few plastics are attacked by some paints, though both acrylic and enamel paints are usually safe. As an example, cellulose paint attacks styrene but not ABS.

Varnishes consist of a solution of resin in a drying oil which, when coated over a surface, dry and harden by evaporation, oxidation or chemical reaction to form a smooth, glossy coating. Epoxy resins are also used to provide a clear finish.

Anti-static
Static can cause problems for those working with plastic materials which are poor conductors. This includes trying to

Figure 10.1 Even painting just a wheel requires careful selection of the best type of paints for the task in hand.

Loctite	Type	Temperature	Features	Uses
8150	Aluminium anti-seize	<900°C	For high loads.	Threads, leadscrews, hinges.
8152	Copper anti-seize	<1100°C	Resists arcing.	Threads, electric contacts.
8155	MoS_2 assembly paste	<450°C	Prevents press fits galling. Reduces wear risk on starting.	Assembling precision components – bearings, gears, bushes on shafts.
8156	Metal-free anti-seize	<900°C	For non-ferrous metals.	Threads, leadscrews, hinges.

Table 10.1 The various uses and characteristics of the Loctite range of assembly pastes. 8150, 8155 and 8156 are also available in aerosols.

polish any transparent item, such as a model windscreen or canopy, not to mention a display cabinet or a clock dome. Anti-static cleaners come in aerosols, bottles and pump/spray containers.

Specialist dust-retaining anti-tack cloths are purpose-made for wiping down models prior to painting. Produced from viscose rayon, they will collect and retain particles of dust from the surface being cleaned.

Acrylics
Acrylic varnishes provide a tough, non-yellowing finish. Both acrylic paints and varnishes are quick drying and resistant to boiling water and alcohol. They are non-inflammable, non-toxic and virtually free of smell. Brushes can be cleaned in water.

Assembly pastes
To prevent seizing during assembly as well as corrosion of parts exposed to adverse conditions, the Loctite range is typical of the currently available products. They are specially designed to be used on static and slow-moving assemblies. These pastes are detailed in Table 10.1.

Celluloses
Cellulose paints, available in tins and aerosol cans from car accessory shops, are a boon in the workshop. The huge range of colours and fast drying are at the root of their popularity. Ensure good ventilation and always use a face mask to avoid inhaling paint, which is also inflammable. Components being painted must first be cleaned and primed.

Creosote
A distillation from coal tar, creosote is a strong-smelling yellow/brown poisonous liquid that is still used to preserve wood for outdoor use. It is popular for treating the exterior of wooden workshops and outdoor railway sleepers.

Enamels
For painting most models, enamel paints are unbeatable. Matt enamels have great covering powers, though they do need protecting with several coats of varnish. They provide excellent results even when applied with a brush. Companies like Humbrol offer a wide range of colours in small tinlets; the more popular ones also in aerosol spray cans and larger tins.

Epoxies
Specialist two-part cold-cure plastic coatings are available for use on wood, cork and plastic laminates. They are clear liquids which do not discolour or darken

with age. They adhere strongly, can be burnished to a mirror finish or rubbed down with steel wool and wax to give a satin finish. Both finishes are resistant to heat, water, solvents and abrasion.

Special aluminium 'powder in epoxy' sprays are ideal for coating most metals and are perfect for repairing damaged galvanised surfaces. The resulting metal surfaces are temperature resistant to a few hundred degrees centigrade.

Epoxy resins, widely used for making GRP, can also be used as a finish on small areas of timber and are an economic way of finishing patterns and forms.

Etchants and primers

The smooth finish of many metals and plastics provides little grip for quite a few adhesives and paints. The use of an etchant, as well as cleaning the surface, also provides for better adhesion.

Primers are painted onto a surface to provide a good anchorage and adhesion for subsequent coats of paint. They must, however, be compatible with the paint. A primer may be colourless, though it is more usually white, pink or silver. Fillers, in the paint sense, are coatings used to fill the grain and help to provide a smooth final surface finish.

Red lead paint is based on lead tetroxide. It is an excellent protective all-in-one primer and paint for iron and steel.

Lacquers

A modern definition of a lacquer is a glossy finish which rapidly dries by evaporation. However, true lacquers are made from natural materials.

Chinese lacquer, a shiny black finish made from the lac plant, was later used to define transparent coatings made with shellac and glossy, pigmented, spirit-based varnishes. Lacquers, renowned for their glossy finish, are rarely weather or

Figure 10.2 A model like this gypsy caravan requires a wide variety of paint and varnish.

solvent resistant. Modern lacquers are based on cellulose, acrylic, melamine or other plastic materials.

Polyurethanes

All the paints and varnishes based on polyurethane have a reputation as hard-wearing and may have a glossy, satin or matt finish. The varnishes do exhibit some yellowing with age or exposure to sunlight. Brushes need to be cleaned with white spirit.

Shellac

Shellac is made from the secretion of the lac insect found in India and south-east Asia. It still has a few applications in the furniture industry and in the manufacture of grinding wheels. It is also used to make sealing wax and some adhesives.

121

Loctite	Type	Temperature	Features	Applications
7800	Zinc	<550°C	Provides cathodic protection.	Primer, protecting metal assemblies and welds.
7801	Aluminium	<500°C	Provides protection against corrosion.	Finishing machined or welded metal parts.
7802	Varnish	<80°C	Long-term protection, easily removed.	Protection of parts and cutting tools in storage.
7803	Metal protect-ion coating	–	Non-drying, tack-free coating.	Long-term protection of machinery/outdoor items.

Table 10.2 Some of the spray protective treatments in the Loctite range.

Silver-loaded conductive paint
Definitely a specialist type of coating, silver-loaded conductive paint is useful for making electrical connections on non-solderable surfaces, pre-coating plastic and ceramic materials prior to electroplating, providing a paint-on electrical screen and producing or repairing tracks on printed circuit boards. Electronic component companies and some model railway shops can supply this type of paint.

Surface treatments
The range of Loctite surface treatments fall into two groups; those included in this section and those which are more readily considered as lubricants. Those listed in Table 10.2 are designed to protect metal-work under adverse conditions.

Solvents
Solvents are liquids which are capable of dissolving another material to form a physical solution. The most common one is water itself. Solvents are widely used in the home workshop for cleaning tasks, diluting other liquids, and for welding plastics. Many of them have unpleasant properties including producing noxious fumes and toxicity. Details of some of the more widely-used ones are shown below.

A number of proprietary cleaners and degreasers are now available, many of which are useful in the home workshop.

These range from domestic products, such as Flash and Mr Muscle, to Swarfega, the green hand-cleaner.

Specific products are also available such as electric-contact cleaners, vehicle-engine cleaners and degreasers, foam cleaners, heavy-duty cleaners, kettle cleaners and oven cleaners. They are ideal for removing dirt, oil and grease, carbon and limescale deposits.

Take care when using some cleaners as they may affect certain plastics. The majority of cleaners are safe on thermo-setting plastics but may damage acrylics and polystyrene. Water-based aqueous cleaners are a good alternative if any doubts exist or solvent has been found to attack a test sample.

Acetone
A colourless but inflammable solvent, acetone is soluble in water. It is perfect for cleaning brushes which have been used either with cellulose paint or polyester resin. It will also remove resin-based flux from printed circuit boards. Take care as it has a low flash point and dissolves many plastics.

Cellulose thinners
Less expensive than acetone, cellulose thinners can be used in the same way to clean brushes after painting with cellulose or working with GRP resin.

Iso propanol
Iso propanol or iso propyl alcohol is a colourless, liquid solvent used for cleaning watch and clock mechanisms. It is also a volatile, poisonous liquid.

Methyl ethyl ketone
This watery, colourless liquid is a powerful solvent which is also inflammable and slightly toxic. It has a similar odour to acetone. It is rapidly being replaced by more environmentally friendly solvents.

Turpentine
An oil extracted from coniferous trees, turpentine is ideal for thinning enamel paints and cleaning brushes.

White spirit
Less expensive than turpentine and sometimes called turpentine substitute, white spirit is economic for cleaning brushes but not recommended for thinning paint.

Paint strippers
The name Nitromors is almost synonymous with paint removal. It is a thick, non-drip liquid, which dissolves paint and varnish from metal, wood and masonry, but is unsuitable for use on GRP.

Fuels

Many different fuels are used by model engineers. Most steam engines are powered by solid fuels, though for smaller ones, liquids are also popular. Gaseous fuels are also used as heat sources and for brazing and welding. The range of calorific values of fuels used in home workshops are shown in Table 10.3.

Liquid fuels
Today, liquid fuels are by far the most numerous and widely used in everyday life.

Fuel	Calorific value
Wood	14MJ/kg
Methanol	20MJ/kg
Methylated spirits	26MJ/kg
Ethanol	27MJ/kg
Coke	28MJ/kg
Anthracite	29MJ/kg
Coal	29MJ/kg
Iso propanol	31MJ/kg
Methane	34MJ/kg
Petrol	42MJ/kg
Diesel	43MJ/kg
Paraffin	44MJ/kg
Acetylene	54MJ/kg
Propane	86MJ/kg
Butane	112MJ/kg
Hexane	164MJ/kg

Table 10.3 The calorific values of a wide range of fuels found in home workshops.

Diesel
A compression ignition engine may run on one of two different forms of diesel fuel. Large engines use the relatively low volatility, oily diesel available from garages. Most small model diesel engines run on a mixture of paraffin, ether and castor oil.

Diesel-based fuels
For running in small engines, one-third paraffin, one-third ether and one-third castor oil works well, but the paraffin content can be increased to 40%, the oil reduced to 25% with the ether content remaining relatively unaltered. Small amounts of specialist additives, such as amyl nitrate, can be added to enhance performance.

Ethanol
Ethyl alcohol, the naturally occurring form of ethanol, is popularly known as alcohol. If it has been produced for non-human consumption (denatured), it is then called industrial alcohol.

Figure 10.3 Methylated spirits is a popular fuel for small hot air and steam engines.

Both industrial alcohol and ethanol are unfit for human consumption. Ethanol mixes with water, absorbs moisture from the atmosphere and has a specific gravity of 0.79.

Methylated spirits

A tax-free purple coloured mixture of around 90% ethyl alcohol and 10% wood alcohol, methylated spirits burns with a bluish flame and ignites at just over 500°C. It is widely used for providing a heat source for small steam boilers and also for cleaning flux off soft-soldered components.

Hexane

A colourless liquid with a low boiling point, hexane is one of the key constituents of petrol. It has an ethereal odour and a specific gravity of 0.66.

Iso propanol

Iso propanol or iso propyl alcohol is a toxic colourless liquid which has a specific gravity of 0.79. As well as a fuel, it is also used as a solvent.

Methanol

Methyl alcohol, commonly called wood alcohol or methanol, is a colourless and poisonous liquid which spontaneously ignites at 457°C and freezes at -98°C. Its specific gravity is 0.795. Methanol burns with a blue, transparent flame and produces carbon dioxide and water as waste products.

A powerful fuel for model two- and four-stroke glow-plug engines, methanol is a slow-burning fuel that is able to tolerate the advanced ignition point found in these engines without pre-igniting. The cooling effect of the methanol is also beneficial.

Methanol is less inflammable than petrol, but a danger is that it burns with an all but invisible flame. Avoid any direct skin contact with methanol, which is absorbed through the skin, as the body does find it difficult to purge.

Methanol-based fuels

Most glow-plug engines run on a mixture of methanol and oil often with a small amount of nitro-methane. Methanol is the fuel. The oil is the lubricant and must be able to mix with methanol. The two popular ones are castor oil, a vegetable extract with exceptional lubricating properties and modern synthetic oils. These latter oils are starting to outperform castor oil.

Most model shops stock a choice of ready-to-use fuel. Two-stroke fuels almost always have a higher oil content than those for use with four-strokes. Keep all containers sealed when not in use and out of the sun. These fuels are all highly inflammable and poisonous. Avoid painful eye contact and, if this occurs, flush out with plenty of clean water.

Fuel mixtures will vary depending on the need of the engine and its operator. For running in most types of engine, an 80% methanol, 20% oil mix is ideal. For more general use, a safe synthetic oil fuel uses 88% methanol and 12% synthetic oil, while a good general-purpose fuel is based on a mixture of 88% methanol, 8% synthetic oil and 4% castor oil.

Nitro-methane

When added to glow fuel, nitro-methane increases power by releasing oxygen which aids combustion. Nitro is normally used only in small amounts, typically 2½% – 10%. Increasing the percentage is costly and normally only done for the smallest, high-performance engines. Idling performance is also improved and

in cold weather, engines are easier to start and run more consistently.

Nitro-methane adds considerably to the risks of internal corrosion on four-stroke engines which rely on leakage of oil past the piston to lubricate the crankshaft, cams, gears and connecting rod. The oil reaching the crankcase contains some burnt fuel residue. This condenses after the engine stops and attacks exposed metal parts. Nitro-methane worsens the corrosion by introducing nitric acid into the fuel residue.

Corrosion inhibitors reduce the damage caused by corrosion on the internal parts of any engine. The two popular methods are by adding some corrosion-inhibiting oil to the fuel or injecting lay-up oil, after-run treatment or a quality machine oil into the crankcase at the end of the running session.

Paraffin

Also called kerosene, paraffin is a hydrocarbon which is refined from petroleum and is a light coloured (usually pink), transparent liquid. It is not as volatile as petrol. It is used in heaters and portable lights; also as a fuel for jet engines and some other internal-combustion engines.

Petrol

Petrol has a specific gravity around 0.75 and is made in a variety of blends to suit the internal-combustion engines fitted to cars, other road-transport vehicles, some railway locomotives and aircraft. Petrol is a petroleum distillate which historically had very small amounts of lead added to increase the octane number and reduce pre-detonation. The addition of lead has been eliminated by improved processing techniques and the inclusion of non-lead based additives. Lead-fee petrol is now available with octane numbers from 91 to 100. Modern unleaded petrol is far

Figure 10.4 Larger scale traction engines and steam locomotives follow prototypical practice in the use of solid fuels.

from the best fuel for low compression-ratio model petrol engines or for vintage and veteran full-size engines.

Solid fuels

Solid fuels comprise wood and its many derivative fossil fuels, which are mainly forms of coal. These fuels are graded by their carbon contents and the higher this figure, the more energy produced per unit of fuel; known as its calorific value. The lower the grade of fuel, the more volatile matter in the form of water (steam) and the oxides of carbon are expelled during combustion.

Anthracite

This variety of coal comes from Wales, Europe and the USA and has a carbon content around 80% but sometimes as high as 95%. It has a semi-metallic sheen and can absorb a high percentage of water. Its calorific value is typically 29MJ/kg and the best anthracite produces only just over 1.5% ash. Pure anthracite burns without producing a smell or smoke.

Charcoal

Produced by slowly burning wood in an oxygen-starved environment, charcoal is a popular fuel today for barbecues as, once well ignited, it burns producing a smoke-free, odourless heat. Lightweight and brittle, charcoal is rarely used in home workshops.

Coal

The main use of coal by model engineers is to provide the heat source for larger-sized static and mobile steam engines. Until the middle of the twentieth century, coal was widely used by industry and by road, rail and sea transportation, as well as in the home, as the primary fuel for providing heat. This popularity rapidly reduced as oil-based derivatives, nuclear and hydro-electric power stations became the norm. A good quality coal contains 60% carbon and less than 8% ash. It releases around 29MJ/kg when burned.

Coke

As a workshop material, coke is most commonly employed as a fuel in a hearth for heating metal. It is the porous, grey fuel, physically stronger than coal, that remains after the volatile elements have been expelled from bituminous coal by heating, without air, to around 1300°C. Coke ignites around 540°C, contains over 85% carbon, burns fast producing little smoke and releasing 28MJ/kg.

Gaseous fuels

Current health and safety regulations mean that gas cylinders used to store acetylene, butane, oxygen and propane must be tested and certified safe on a regular basis. Refills for acetylene and oxygen are available from specialist gas suppliers while butane and propane are readily purchased from caravan and some DIY stores.

The cylinder colour coding must also be correct; a black top on the long, thin cylinder for acetylene and a white top for oxygen, a blue container for butane and red one for propane. There is an initial rental charge for each cylinder which, when empty is exchanged for a full one for the price of the gas.

Compressed gases are dangerous and must be stored away from any risk of fire and where they will not negate any household insurance. In addition, no grease must be used on the fixtures or fittings of oxygen bottles. It is also worth remembering that butane and propane are heavier than air and that a leak can result in an explosion if there is not adequate ventilation at floor level.

Acetylene
Burned in oxy-acetylene welders and flame cutters, acetylene produces a really hot flame. When mixed with oxygen it burns at 3500°C. It is a colourless gas supplied in large refillable cylinders and in aerosols for miniature oxy-acetylene torches. It burns with a bright luminous but sooty flame in air and is explosive with the right mixture; around 8% gas, 92% air.

Butane
Burning at a relatively low temperature, butane is available in small, disposable containers, which are ideal heat sources for steam boilers. It also comes in larger, refillable cylinders. In every case, these cylinders are painted pale blue for identification of their contents. Butane tends

to freeze if too rapidly taken out of its storage container. It has an exceptionally high calorific value of 112MJ/kg.

Methane
Natural gas, now piped to the majority of homes in the UK, contains between 70% and 90% methane with up to 20% propane and traces of other gases.

Propane
As a fuel for brazing, as a source of heat for steam boilers and as a fuel for model turbojets, propane is readily available from DIY stores and stores supplying the camping and caravan markets. Its calorific value is 86MJ/kg and it is less inclined than butane to freeze as it expands out of its container. A range of cylinder sizes is painted red for identification purposes.

Other gases
Not all gases used in the home workshop are fuels. Some are used in welding to support combustion or as inert gases.

Argon
One of the five rare gases, argon is an inert gas amounting to about one percent of the atmosphere. It is used to shield the electrode from the air in TIG and MIG welding.

CO^2
A dense gas breathed out by all animals and a by-product of combustion, carbon dioxide is an inert gas used as an alternative to argon for TIG and MIG welding. It is also used, in compressed form, as a fuel for small CO_2 powered engines.

Oxygen
The Earth's atmosphere contains 21% oxygen, without which no-one could live. It is also a major constituent of water. It is a colourless, odourless gas. Relatively

pure oxygen significantly increases the temperature of combustion and this is used to provide welding temperatures. However, compressed oxygen has its dangers. Do not use grease on fittings or pipe work. Compressed oxygen is available in large steel cylinders and also in aerosol-sized containers.

Lubricants

Lubricants in the home workshop fall into one of three categories; oils, greases and cutting lubricants/suds. These materials are either derived from animals, vegetables or minerals; the last being almost entirely derived from petroleum. The choice of individual lubricant depends on the operating temperature range, the speed and duty, the level of vibration, the materials being lubricated and possible contact with other chemicals. General-purpose lubricating oils, like 3-in-1, also contain rust inhibitors.

Cutting lubricants

Cutting oils reduce friction by lubricating the cutting tool/work interface. They are usually heavy oils or compounds and also carry away a lot of heat, increasing tool life. They may contain some resin to improve cutting action and a corrosion inhibitor. They differ from the soluble oil used in suds to keep the work piece cool. However, there is no sharp divide between cutting oils and soluble oils since both provide lubrication.

Lard oil is excellent for cutting but, because of its cost, it is usually mixed with mineral or vegetable oil. It is used for machining copper alloys or steel where a good surface finish is needed. A mixture of lard oil and paraffin is also good for cutting aluminium and monel. Ordinary

mineral oils are satisfactory for light cuts combining lubrication with some cooling. For brass, an emulsion of oil in soapy water is popular. Paraffin and turpentine both work well when hand-reaming brass, while a mix of tallow and graphite is best with cast iron. A mix of turpentine and lard-oil is fine for copper while paraffin is recommended for both cutting and threading aluminium. For screw cutting, a mixture of paraffin and vegetable oil works well but for fine threads, a heavy oil mixed with white lead is worth trying.

Soluble oils

Soluble cutting oils emulsify easily and can be mixed with water in proportions usually lying between 20:1 and 50:1. Normally, general-purpose, light/medium cutting oils suffice for home workshop operations. Typical examples include Castrol Cooledge B1, particularly suitable for use when working with steel or cast iron, and Castrol Hysol G which is equally suited to ferrous and non-ferrous metals as well as perspex. Rocol Ultracut 250 Plus comes in standard and hard-water variants, as does Ultracut 280A Plus for use on aluminium and other non-ferrous metals. A semi-synthetic alternative is Ultracut 390H which includes 40% oil content. Always add the oil to water, not the other way round.

Tapping fluids

For drilling, tapping and reaming, specialist hand-applied lubricants, such as Rocol's RTD range are easy to apply and rapidly flow to the cutting zone. A cutting oil like Loctite 8030 is suitable for drilling and tapping steel, especially stainless steel and most non-ferrous metals.

Graphite

In the form of graphite, carbon is a first-class lubricant. Graphite-loaded greases

Loctite	Type	Temperature	Features	Uses
8101	Chain lubricant	175°C	Anti-fling, water resistant.	Chains and open gears.
8102	High performance	200°C	High loads at high speeds, works in high humidities.	Roller/plain bearings, heavily loaded open gears, slideways.
8103	MoS$_2$	150°C	High and shock loads, vibration.	Cylindrical taper, roller and plain bearings, splines, lead screws, slideways.
8106	Multi purpose	150°C	General use.	Roller and plain bearings, open gears, slideways.

Table 10.4 The key features and uses of the Loctite range of greases.

are widely available and graphite-loaded metals are used to make self-lubricating bearings and bushes.

Grease

Almost all greases used for lubrication in the home workshop, where speeds are relatively slow, are a compound of mineral oil and soap. Well known brands include Castrol LM, Esso Beacon EP2, Mobil Mobilux EP2 and Shell Alvania EP2. In addition, Myford can supply Castrol Moly, Graphite, Water Pump and Red Rubber Greases as well as Copper Grease. For lubricating plastic-to-plastic and metal-to-plastic gears it is better to use Castrol Alpha gel, Castrol Spheerol AP1, Mobil Glygol 00, Shell Alvania R1 or Shell Tivella comp A.

The Loctite range of greases includes mineral- and synthetic-based oils. The key characteristics are given in Table 10.4.

Graphite grease contains up to 10% amorphous graphite and is particularly useful for bearings exposed to the damp. Silicone greases are excellent in conditions where speeds and temperatures are high. They also resist water washing them out but are limited in the loads they can withstand.

The Rocol range of standard Sapphire greases include Sapphire 1, which is a multi-purpose lubricant designed to protect plain, ball and roller bearings operating in the temperature range -30°C to +150°C. Sapphire Hi-speed 2 has a top speed capability unlikely to be exceeded by most modellers.

Hydraulic oil

Ordinary hydraulic oil is a fine general-purpose lubricant, especially as it always contains a corrosion inhibitor. Its use is essential in any hydraulically-powered machinery or model. Proprietary brands include Esso Noto H32, Esso Univis N32, Mobil 13M and Shell Tellus T32.

Lubricating oil

The purpose of lubricating oil is to keep moving parts from physical contact with each other by forming a thin film between them. It must be able perform under high pressure and temperature. Transfer of heat is also an important attribute and larger machines may use an oil cooler.

Oil is employed for lubricating bearings, gear trains and other rubbing machine parts. Most oils are heavy distillates of petroleum, though a few still come from animal or vegetable sources. They may be light, medium or heavy grade.

Steam cylinder lubricants tend to have 5 – 10% fatty acid vegetable oils added, though silicone-based oils are preferred for extremes of high or low temperature. Molybdenum disulphide, added to oils like Molyslip and anti-friction coatings such as Loctite 8191, further reduces friction. Some coatings are produced with PTFE added to minimise friction.

Typical gear oils from major suppliers include Castrol Magna BD86 and CF220, Esso Spartan EP220, Mobil Mobilgear 630 and Shell Omala 220. Myford offers Nuto H32, Febis K68 and Nuray 100 lubricating oils as well as Rocol's Slideway Lubricant and Belt Dressing Spray. Rocol produce a range of gear oils under their Sapphire Hi-Torque series with viscosities in five ranges from 100 to 680.

Castor oil
Castor oil is a pale yellow/brown syrupy liquid which is used as an exceptionally efficient lubricant. It is refined from the castor bean which grows in the tropics.

It does, however, gum up internal combustion engines that are not used for some time. The castor oil solidifies on the moving parts and can cause problems with piston rings and ball-races when the engine is restarted, unless the residue is first flushed out. It also produces a hard carbon layer on hot parts of the engine which is difficult to remove. Castor oil is increasingly being replaced by mineral oil substitutes.

Machinery protection
Lathe slideways and other machine tool parts are prone to rusting, particularly in those home workshops which are liable to damp. Rocol's Ultraglide X5 is a typical product which provides lubrication and corrosion protection.

Molybdenum disulphide
A material with a graphite-like structure, molybdenum disulphide is a first-class lubricant or coating, performing better than graphite under high pressure.

Steam oil
GP 1000 is a lubricating oil which has been specially designed for use on reciprocating steam engines. Although quite viscous, it is an excellent lubricant but is not suitable for use in other applications.

WD40
Available in aerosol cans, WD40 is a low viscosity, water-displacing, non-conducting, silicone-free lubricant which is ideal for freeing rusted parts and for drying out electrical equipment. Loctite 8201 is a similar product. Both products will stop a file clogging when working aluminium.

Watch and clock oils and greases
These lubricants are specially formulated to avoid evaporation and spreading. A wide range of oils is designed to cope with different sizes of clock or watch, pressures, bearing materials and range of temperatures. Those produced by Microtime, Moebius and Windles are well known. Specialist greases are used on springs and winding mechanisms. Some include graphite but waterproof greases are silicone based. Cuyper, Microtime and Moebius all make a range of these greases.

Miscellaneous other materials

Antifreeze
To prevent frost damage in water-based cooling systems, or heating systems which are switched off, liquid additives are needed to reduce the freezing point without decreasing the boiling point or causing corrosion. There are three popular additives.

The first is methanol. A 50% mixture with water provides protection down to minus 30°C. However, the methanol needs frequent topping up due to loss from the mixture by evaporation.

One alternative which does not suffer from evaporation is glycerol. It is effective down to minus 22°C when used in a fifty-fifty mix. It is a viscous liquid, however, which may cause problems in the narrow coolant passages of small models.

The final choice, and probably the best, is ethylene glycol which has a lower freezing point and does not evaporate. It is more costly and softens natural rubber tubes. A 25% solution provides protection down to minus 20°C.

Concrete

A construction material used, among other things, to build home workshops and outdoor railway structures, concrete is usually made from Portland cement, sand, gravel and water. Crushed stone, slag or vermiculite may replace the gravel.

Concrete is readily moulded into any shape and the surface smoothed with a trowel. It quickly hardens and precautions must be taken to avoid too rapid drying out in warm conditions and protection from frost if cold. When set, concrete is strong in compression and, with gravel aggregate typically weighs around

Figure 10.5 Constructing an outside railway almost always seems to involve laying concrete.

2500kg/cu m. The use of steel reinforcing bars converts concrete into a composite material that is also strong in tension.

Plaster of Paris

This white powder is dehydrated gypsum of calcium sulphate. When mixed with water, it solidifies and sets firmly. It is useful for making moulds and casts that can be strengthened by the inclusion of one or more layers of muslin or bandage.

Plasterboard, made from gypsum and faced on each side with paper, provides a fire-resistant lining for workshop buildings. It is also available with aluminium foil on one side to help reduce heat loss from the building.

APPENDIX 1

Safety

Overview

Few people enjoy reading about safety, yet many workshop materials can inflict damage if misused. Although some items are inflammable, model making does not normally create a serious fire risk. However, a sensible approach is needed when storing materials, particularly fuels, gases and solvents, to avoid negating any household insurance. Some other dangers include the potential for asthma attacks, bruises, cuts, dermatitis, explosions, eye and respiratory irritation, chemical and heat burns, poisonous fumes from gases, liquids and overheated solids, and even suffocation. However, model engineering is still a very low-risk hobby when it is compared with cycling, car travel, swimming in the sea or mountaineering.

Solids

Probably the commonest dangers when using metal in a home workshop are dropping a piece of metal on part of the anatomy, being cut by swarf or getting burned when heating metal.

Because they are excellent conductors, metals quickly get hot when heated. Wear protective gloves when holding one end of a piece of metal. Many plastics emit noxious fumes if burned, so take particular care during disposal. PTFE gives off poisonous fumes when set alight or heated above 270°C, so extra care is needed when machining this material. The same is true of zinc and zinc-plated materials like galvanised steel but at a rather higher temperature of just over 400°C.

When heating plastics to form them, these materials retain heat for a long time. Again wear thick protective gloves. Unpleasant fumes may be given off, so that adequate ventilation is essential, as are facilities for smothering any accidental fire. When thermoplastics are heated they melt and drip blobs of plastic which can cause nasty burns or ignite whatever they fall on.

Working with cadmium-bearing silver solders can produce poisonous fumes when heated, particularly above 767°C; the melting point of cadmium. Adequate ventilation and rapid working, avoiding prolonged heating, will avoid this danger but a better alternative is to use cadmium-free solders.

Working with GRP or silicone rubber
With a few simple precautions, handling GRP or silicone rubber is safe. Follow

the manufacturer's instructions and wear rubber or plastic gloves when working with these materials. Their catalysts are both inflammable and will attack skin, the eyes and mouth. Quickly wash any catalyst off skin. Rinse eyes under running water and get immediate medical attention.

Do not inhale the inflammable vapours emitted by GRP polyester resin, do not smoke and work in a well ventilated area. Acetone for brush cleaning is also inflammable. Store all these materials safely when not in use.

Liquids

As a sensible precaution, keep containers of liquids so their labels can be read and store them out of reach of children. Always follow the manufacturer's instructions and wear protective goggles, overalls and disposable gloves when appropriate.

Ensure there is good ventilation as some processes produce extremely hazardous fumes while others give off potentially explosive hydrogen gas. Quite a number of liquids are also highly inflammable and create toxic gas when burned. Take care not to expose them to sparks or flames. Unfortunately the fumes from a few chemicals are highly addictive. To avoid solvent abuse, limit access to them.

Some chemicals mentioned in Chapter 9 are acids, others are very alkaline; both highly corrosive. Always wear protective clothing when working with them and avoid splashing them. Always slowly add acid to water, stirring continuously to avoid overheating; never the other way round. Stand plastic containers in an outer tank of cold water.

Mercury is highly toxic but there is little alternative for filling a mercury-in-glass barometer. Liquefying metals for casting results in two hazards. The first is the danger of getting burned by the hot metal. Not as obvious is the need to have the

mould for the hot metal perfectly dry. Any damp will immediately be turned to steam by the hot metal. The expanding steam can project molten metal with explosive force for a significant distance.

Fumes from most superglues are unpleasant and these adhesives should only be used in a well-ventilated area. Their effect can be cumulative to an extent that makes their use impossible. Remember, too, their ability to glue fingers, or other parts of the body, to almost anything else. Epoxy and other resins can aggravate or cause dermatitis and eczema so avoid skin contact.

Most plastics in liquid form such as adhesives, resins and solvents, are dangerous if swallowed, inhaled or if they get into eyes or repeated contact with the skin.

Gases

A number of gases may be stored/used in the home workshop. These commonly include acetylene, butane, propane and oxygen. The first three are inflammable and explosive in a fire. Gases which are heavier than air may pool on the floor, ready to explode at the first sign of a spark or naked flame. Ground-level ventilation will avoid a build-up of gas in the event of a leak. All these gases require appropriate precautions to be taken and the fitting of blow-back units to gas burners to protect against fracture of the flexible gas hose. The last gas, oxygen, makes any fire worse. Never use oil or grease on oxygen-bottle connectors.

Dust and breakages

Sanding wood or plastics, and this includes composite materials, produces dust which should not be inhaled. Wear a protective mask if any significant amount of dust is likely to be created. Take particular care with any fillers and hardened mixes that contain micro-balloons. Some of the more brittle plastics will shatter if they are over-enthusiastically worked, so it is a good idea to wear safety glasses for protection.

Working with some types of wood can produce eye or respiratory irritation, or even dermatitis. However, unless planning a significant amount of woodworking with the few timbers that may cause these problems, this should not be a concern.

Disposal

Disposing of metal and wood presents few problems and, in any case, most council tips accept poisons, like spent pickle or mercury, provided they are not in commercial amounts. Many plastics burn readily and emit plenty of smoke that is sometimes toxic. Most plastics are not biodegradable so dispose of scrap in a rubbish bin, rather than trying to burn it.

Fire extinguishers

It is only common sense to keep a fire extinguisher handy in any workshop. There are three main classes or types of extinguisher:

- Carbon dioxide, which smother the fire.
- Foam and powder, which insulate the fire from air.
- Chemical, which react with the products of combustion to terminate the combustion reaction.

Water should not be used to deal with electrical fires, where there is electrical wiring or where there is a burning liquid such as petrol or paraffin. A powder-based extinguisher is likely to be most effective in a home workshop and make the least mess. It is also worth having a first aid kit to treat cuts, bruises, heat and chemical burns.

APPENDIX 2

Glossary of abbreviations and terms

AISI. American Iron and Steel Institute Standards.

Aliphatic. Having a straight, chain-like molecular structure.

Alloy. A metal consisting of an intimate association of one metal with one or more other metals or non-metals, such as brass and steel. The result may be a compound, a mixture or a solid solution.

Anodising. A method of protecting a metal surface, normally aluminium, against corrosion by chemical or electrolytic action. Thin films may be coloured.

ASTM. American Society for Testing and Materials.

Atom. The smallest particle which can take part in a chemical reaction.

Austenite. A solid solution of carbon in gamma iron.

Bainite. A mixture of ferrite plates and short cementite rods.

BDMS. Black or bright-drawn mild steel.

BR. Butadiene rubber.

Brittleness. The property of breaking without visible warning or deformation.

BS. British Standards.

BS EN. European Standards.

°C. Degree centigrade.

CAB. Cellulose acetate butyrate.

Calorific value. The amount of heat produced when a fuel is completely burned. It is usually expressed in MJ/m^3.

Catalyst. A substance that speeds up or slows down a chemical reaction, which itself undergoes no permanent chemical change.

CBN. Cubic boron nitride.

cc. Cubic centimetre.

CDA. Copper Development Association Standards.

Cementite. Iron carbide.

CSM. Chopped strand mat.

Compressibility. The extent to which a material, such as a gasket, is compressed by a specified load.

Conductivity. The rate at which any material conducts heat or electricity. The finest known conductor, silver, is used as a reference.

CPVC. Chlorinated polyvinyl chloride.

CR. Chloroprene rubber.

Creep. The gradual and continuous distortion of a material under continued load, usually at high temperatures.

Curie point. The temperature above which iron ceases to be magnetic.

Density. The ratio of the mass of a material to its volume, usually expressed in g/cc^3.

Ductility. The ability to be deformed permanently by tension without rupture.

Elastic limit. The greatest unit stress a

material can withstand without permanent deformation.

Elasticity. The ability to resume its original form after removal of the load which has produced a change in form. A highly-elastic substance is very easy to deform and quickly recovers.

Elongation. The increase in length of a bar or section under load, expressed as a percentage difference between the original length and the length at the moment of rupture or at a specific strain.

EPNS. Electro-plated nickel-silver.

Eutectoid point. The critical temperature at which the structure of a material changes. The temperature for steel is 723°C.

Ferrite. A solution of carbon in alpha iron.

g. Gram

g/cc³. Grams per cubic centimetre.

GRP. Glass reinforced plastic.

Hardness. The property of solids that indicates their solidity and firmness in outline. A hard substance does not readily indent.

Heartwood. The fully-developed wood which supports and gives rigidity to a tree.

HSS. High speed steel.

Hygroscopic. Readily absorbing and retaining moisture.

Impact strength. The force required to break a material when suddenly struck a blow.

ISO. International Standards Organisation.

kg/m³. Kilograms per cubic metre.

Magnet. A mass of iron or other material which attracts or repels other masses of iron and which exerts a force on a nearby current-carrying conductor.

Malleability. The property of permanent deformation by compression without rupture; the ability to be hammered into thin sheets.

Martensite. A super-saturated solid solution of carbon in ferrite.

MDF. Medium-density fibre board.

MEK. Methyl ethyl ketone.

MF. Melamine formaldehyde.

MJ/m³. Mega joules per cubic metre.

mm. Millimetre

Modulus of elasticity. The ratio of the unit stress to the unit strain in tension or compression within the elastic limit without fracture.

Molecule. An atom or group of atoms that can exist independently and has characteristic properties of the basic material.

N/mm². Newtons per square millimetre.

NBR. Nitrile rubber.

Octane number. A measure of the detonation characteristics of petrol in an engine.

Pearlite. A mixture of both ferrite and cementite.

PEEK. Polyether ether ketone.

PGMS. Precision ground mild steel.

Plastic. A generic name for an organic material, usually a synthetic or semi-synthetic polymer.

Plasticity. The ability of a material to permanently deform at low load.

Polymer. A long chain molecule built up by repetition of groups of atoms. The molecular size of any polymer helps to determine the mechanical properties of the plastic.

PPVC. Plasticised polyvinyl chloride.

PTFE. Polytetrafluoroethylene.

PVC. Polyvinyl chloride or vinyl.

Rare earth metals. A group of metals which are hard to extract, rather than rare. The list includes cerium, didymium, dysprosium, erbium, europium, gadolinium, holmium, lanthanum, lutetium, neodymium, praseodymium, rhenium, scandium, thorium, thulium, ytterbium and yttrium.

Sapwood. The immature and newly-matured wood in the outer part of a tree.

SBR. Styrene-butadiene rubber.

Shrinkage. The reduction in the dimensions of a material.

Softening point. The softening point for thermoplastic materials is the temperature at which a flat-ended needle of $1mm^2$ area will penetrate a specimen to a depth of 1 mm under a load of 1,000g when the temperature of the specimen is raised at a constant rate of 50°C/hour.

Solubility. Capacity for being dissolved in a liquid so that it will not separate out on standing, except the excess over the percentage which the liquid (solvent) will dissolve.

Solvent. A liquid capable of dissolving another material to form a solution.

Specific gravity. The ratio of the weight of a given volume of a material to the weight of an equal volume of pure water at 4°C.

Specific heat. The number of calories required to raise the temperature of 1g of a material 1°C.

Stiffness. The ability of a material to resist deflection.

Strain. The distortion in a material when a load is applied.

Strength. The ability of a material to resist an applied load.

Stress. Force, or load, per unit area.

Tensile strength. The maximum tensile load per square unit of cross section that a material is able to withstand.

Thermal conductivity. The number of calories transmitted per second between the opposite faces of a cube, 10mm x 10mm x 10mm, when the temperature difference between the opposite faces of the cube is 1°C.

Thermal expansion. The coefficient of linear thermal expansion is the increase in unit length for each 1°C temperature change.

Thermoplastic. A plastic capable of being melded and remoulded without rupture by heat and pressure.

Thermosetting plastic. A plastic which sets into a hard solid not capable of being remoulded.

Toughness. The ability of a material to resist impact, or absorb energy, without fracturing.

Ultimate strength. The stress, calculated from the maximum applied load and the original area of cross section, which causes fracture of the material.

UTS. Ultimate tensile strength.

UPVC. Unplasticised polyvinyl chloride.

UF. Urea formaldehyde.

Yield point. The minimum tensile stress required to produce continuous deformation of a solid material.

APPENDIX 3

Metric/imperial conversions

The world is rapidly becoming a metric one. Even in the United States, the bastion of imperial units, metric units are now widely used by many industries. Almost all materials are only produced with metric dimensions. As a result, almost all the units used in this volume are metric ones.

There are still many machine tools and measuring instruments, not to mention model engineering plans that were produced in the old imperial days. People still need to build models from such plans, despite the fact that the availability of imperial-dimensioned materials, already difficult, is likely to become more so. For those who need them, particularly those using imperial machinery and tools, the following conversion tables should be of assistance.

Length

	millimetre mm	centimetre cm	metre m	thou	inch in	foot ft
1 millimetre	1	0.1	0.001	39.4	0.0394	0.0033
1 centimetre	10	1	0.01	394	0.394	0.033
1 metre	1000	100	1	–	39.37	3.28
1 thou	0.0254	–	–	1	0.001	–
1 inch	25.4	2.54	0.0254	1000	1	0.0833
1 foot	304.8	30.48	0.3048	–	12	1

Area

	square millimetre mm²	square centimetre cm²	square metre m²	square inch in²	square foot ft²
1 mm²	1	0.01	–	0.0015	0.000011
1 cm²	100	1	0.0001	0.15	0.0011
1 m²	–	0.01	1	1550	10.7639
1 in²	645.2	6.452	0.00065	1	0.00694
1 ft²	92903	929.03	0.0929	144	1

Volume

	cubic centimetre cc	cubic metre m³	millilitre ml	litre l	cubic inch in³	cubic yard yd³	gallon gall
1 cc	1	10⁻⁶	1	0.001	0.061	–	0.00022
1 m³	10⁶	1	10⁶	1000	61024	1.31	220
1 ml	1	10⁻⁶	1	0.001	0.061	–	0.00022
1 l	1000	0.001	1000	1	61.02	0.0011	0.22
1in³	16.39				1		
1yd³	–	0.765	–	756	46656	1	285.7
1gall	4546	0.0045	4546	4.546	279.2	0.0035	1

Mass

	gram g	kilogram kg	ounce oz	pound lb
1 gram	1	1000	0.035	0.0022
1 kilogram	1000	1	35.27	2.2046
1 ounce	28.3	0.0283	1	0.0625
1 pound	453.6	0.4536	16	1

Density

	g/cc	g/ml	lb/gall	lb/ft³
g/cc	1	1	10.02	62.43
g/ml	1	1	10.02	62.43
lb/gall	0.099	0.099	1	6.23
lb/ft³	0.016	0.016	0.16	1

Stress

	Newtons/mm² N/mm²	tonf/in²	lbf/in²
N/mm²	1	0.065	145
tonf/in²	15.44	1	2240
lbf/in²	0.007	0.00045	1

Calorific value

	Mega joules/kilogram MJ/kg	British thermal units/pound BTU/lb
Mega joules/kg	1	2090
BTU/lb	0.00045	1

Temperature

Fahrenheit temperature $= 32 + (1.8 \times$ centigrade temperature)

Centigrade temperature $=$ (Fahrenheit temperature $- 32) \times 5 \div 9$

APPENDIX 4

List of useful addresses

Abrasives
CSM Just Abrasives, 95-96, Lewis Rd., Brighton, East Sussex, BN2 3QA.
  Perma-grit Tools, The White Ho., Pointon, Sleaford, Lincs., NG34 0LX.
Abrasives, adhesives, lubricants & metal
J&L Industrial Supply, 7 Pacific Avenue, Wednesbury, West Midlands, WS10 7WP.
Abrasives, lubricants & plating chemicals
Shesto Ltd, Unit 2, Sapcote Trading Centre, 374, High Rd., Willesden, NW10 2DH.
Adhesives
Deluxe Materials (Models) UK, Thornton Ho., Soke Rd., Silchester, Berks., RG7 2NS.
Adhesives, coatings and plastics
W Hobby Ltd., Knight's Hill Sq., London, SE27 0HH.
Adhesives, lubricants & putties
Loctite UK Ltd., Watchmead, Welwyn Garden City, Herts., AL7 1JB.
Ceramics
Precision Ceramics, 86, Lower Tower St., Birmingham, B19 3PA.
Cleaners, fillers, polishes and solders
Frost Restoration Techniques Ltd., Crawford St., Rochdale, Lancs., OL16 5NU.
Metal and engineering materials
A.J. Reeves & Co. Ltd., Holly Lane, Marston Green, Birmingham, B37 7AW.
  MACC Model Engineering Supplies, 45A, Saville St., Macclesfield, SK11 7LQ.

Metals, plastics and other materials
Electromail, PO Box 99, Corby, Northants, NN17 9RS.
  Maplin MPS, PO Box 777, Rayleigh, Essex, SS6 8LU.
Metals, plastics and solders
Bruce Engineering, Hollow Tree, Penny Lane, Shepperton, Middx., TW17 8NF.
Hobby books and magazines
Nexus Special Interests Ltd., Nexus Ho., Azalea Drive, Swanley, Kent, BR8 8HU.
Lubricants
Myford Ltd., Beeston, Nottingham, NG9 1ER.
  ROCOL Ltd., ROCOL Ho., Swillington, Leeds, LS26 8BS.
Non-ferrous metals
Colombia Metals, 19, High St., Earls Barton, Northants., NN6 0JG.
Silicone rubber
Alec Tiranti Ltd., 70, High St., Theale, Reading, Berks., RG7 5AR.
Solders
TEC-NICK, 92-98 Haltwhistle Rd, South Woodham Ferrers, Essex CM3 5ZF.
Timber
John Boddy's Fine Wood & Tool Store Ltd., Riverside Sawmills, Boroughbridge, N. Yorks. YO5 9LJ.
  Craft Supplies Ltd., The Mill, Millers Dale, Nr Buxton, Derbys, SK17 8SN.

APPENDIX 5

Bibliography

Dictionary of Science and Technology. Prof Peter Walker (Larousse 1995)

Engineering Materials Technology 2nd Ed. W. Bolton (B-H Newnes 1993)

Fuel and Energy. J.H. Harker and J.R. Backhurst (Academic Press Inc 1981)

Materials and their Uses. W. Bolton (Butterworth-Heinemann Ltd. 1996)

Materials Handbook 14th Ed. Brady, Clauser and Vaccari (McGraw Hill 1997)

Metals in the Service of Man. Arthur Street and William Alexander (Penguin Books 1994)

Model Engineer's Handbook 3rd Ed. Tubal Cain (Nexus Special Interests 1996)

Structure and Properties of Engineering Alloys. William Smith (McGraw-Hill Inc 1993)

Plastics for Modellers. Alex Weiss (Nexus Special Interests 1998)

Properties of Engineering Materials 2nd Ed. R.A. Higgins (Edward Arnold 1994)

Steels: Metallurgy and Applications. D.T. Llewellyn (Butterworth-Heinemann Ltd. 1994)

Woodwork in Theory and Practice. John A Walton (Australian Publishing Company 1974)

Workshop Practice Series:

   No 9 Soldering and Brazing. Tubal Cain (Nexus Special Interests 1988)

   No 11 Electroplating. J Poyner (Nexus Special Interests 1991)

   No 21 Adhesives and Sealants. Dave Lammas (Nexus Special Interests 1991)

INDEX

146